Beyond Space

Formerly
"Advaita Vedanta and Modern science"
By
John Dobson *Founder of the San Francisco*
Sidewalk Astronomers
& Dr. Ruth Ballard PhD.

Published by
Temple Universal Publishing
www.templeuniversal.com
First Printing 2004

ISBN 0-9728051-9-2

Beyond Space and Time

By

John Dobson

&

Dr. Ruth Ballard

"Baburam, I want to go to every nook
and corner of this world and tell them
they are Brahman, but the body gets in
the way."

Swami Vivekananda, July 2nd, 1902
(Two days before he passed away)

This book is written for the traveler who would know where he is going before he sets out upon his journey.

Summary

We don't have two worlds one for the scientists and one for the mystics. There's only one of it. And if the mystics are right in their descriptions, and if the scientists are right in theirs, we need only a translator and a dictionary of both languages. Fortunately for us, John Dobson and Ruth Ballard lived and worked in both camps, and know both languages, so they undertook the task of translating.

But to succeed in joining the descriptions by the physicists and the mystics they had to start far below the scientist's descriptions and they got there through Einstein's 1905 equations, his physics and his geometry.

Preface

Really, I suppose, this book arose through a collision of European and Asiatic interpretations of their observations of the real world. In Europe, when a man dies, we say he gives up the ghost. The body is taken to be real. In India, they say he gives up the body. The soul is taken to be real. To the European, the world is made of ninety-two chemical elements. To the Asiatic, it is made of only five. The Europeans take science seriously, but they take philosophy with a grain of salt. After all, weren't the philosophers only guessing? But the Hindus take philosophy seriously, and they take science with some salt. After all, isn't the world unreal? Yet, although these differences in interpretation are obvious to all, there cannot be two real worlds, one for the East and one for the West. As Kipling said in

Beyond Space and Time

"The Ballad of East and West," the first line of which is usually quoted out of context:

> ... But there is neither East nor West,
> Border, nor Breed, nor Birth,
> When two strong men stand face to face,
> Tho' they come from the ends of the earth!

Since there can be only one real world, it must be that our various descriptions and interpretations of it can be reconciled if we can understand the other fellow's language and the observations on which his descriptions and interpretations are based.

Fortunately for me, I was educated partly by Europeans and Americans, and partly by Asiatics, and my Sanskrit is better than my Greek. I mention these two ancient languages because the problem of misinterpretation goes back, before the development of modern Indo-European languages, to a time when Greek and Sanskrit were the spoken languages on the caravan route from India to Asia Minor, and on the water routes from India to Greece.

Preface

It was along these routes that the old five-element theory most probably migrated from India to Greece through Thales of Miletus, about 600 BC. At that time, Thales was a Greek mercenary, fighting for Egypt in Babylonia, while Indian traders were in Babylon. My first important clue to the solution of the problem of the reconciliation of the Eastern and Western interpretations came when I was studying the Greek version of this old theory. Having been trained in physics and chemistry at the University of California, I had been taught to laugh the old five-element theory to scorn. After all, even the early atomic tables ran to ninety-two chemical elements. But by the time I got around to studying the early Greek version, I had already been exposed to the Sanskrit version which, of course, is much older. In the ancient Sanskrit, each of the five elements is associated with one of our five senses of perception, and it became at once obvious to me that the elements they spoke of were not substances, like the elements of chemistry, but five kinds of energy. My problem was simply to identify them. It was

Beyond Space and Time

John Dalton who borrowed the term "element" from the older theory, because in his day the European theory had become so garbled that its adherents could no longer "show their wares." In Sanskrit, Akasha (gravity) is associated with the ear (the saccule), Vayu (kinetic energy) with the skin (temperature), Tejas (radiation) with the eye, and Ap and Prithivi (electricity and magnetism) with the tongue and the nose. (Protons taste sour.) The conflict was not between theories but only over the meanings of words.

INERT MATTER?

The history of human knowledge reads like a mystery story. It begins with many problems, and with a smattering of clues, some important, some obvious, some trivial and some misleading. Only at the end does the whole picture emerge, only after the plot has been very much thickened by overlooking the obvious and following clues which were either trivial or misleading. In what appears to us to have been the dark ages of human understanding, matter was thought to be inert.

Preface

It is often taught that way in school. But this notion arises from a misleading clue. Matter moves by itself under the influence of gravity. It is self-impelled by its own gravitational field. But we are born on a planet where the action of what we call gravity is impeded by the solid rocky structure beneath our feet, giving rise to the impression that matter is inert. As a consequence of this early misunderstanding, all the motions of matter were attributed to the actions of gods and goddesses. Matter was thought to move, not by its own nature, but under the influence of forces from outside, forces initiated by living beings. There was a sun god, a moon god, a wind god, and a storm god. There was a god for gravity and a god for electricity. There was even a god for inertia, to keep moving objects in motion, because it was thought that matter, being inert, would come to a stop by itself. It was felt then, as it is felt now, that each of us, as a living organism, has his or her own "vital energy." It was not recognized that our so-called "vital energy" is not our own but comes from eating and breathing. It was not understood then that the

Universe is "ert," and that the reason we seem to have "vital energy" is because all living beings live in a cascade of increasing entropy by directing bits of the increase through their forms. In those days the discrimination was between the quick and the dead. We were the quick, and matter was the dead. We were the movers of matter; and if matter was found to move without intervention by us, then it must have been moved by gods and goddesses much like ourselves. Quaint. But at least their solution contained within it the recognition that their concept of matter could not explain its behavior. The problem of *why* matter moved remained unsolved.

HOW AND WHY MATTER MOVES

Rejecting the notion of gods and goddesses as the movers of matter, the European scientists sought the solution in the detailed investigation of *how* matter moves. This new attack proved very rewarding, and gradually the "why" questions slipped into the background. Although they were never laid to rest, it was hoped that the "why" questions

Preface

would somehow be answered through the study of how matter moved. Sir Isaac Newton even felt that the "why" questions belonged in the domain of theology, and that only the "how" questions belonged in the domain of science. In a sense it was a step backwards, partly because the European theology of his day was still overrun by the quaint old notion that "vital energy" was the mover of matter, and, therefore, on a grand scale, the Universe must be moved by the "vital energy" of a personal God. But at least, within this view, the origin of the Universe lay outside of physics. The causation of our physics was restricted to the transformations of matter and energy, and it was recognized that matter and energy cannot arise through transformations within that matter and that energy. It was recognized that the origin of the Universe cannot be found within the framework of transformational causation. The problem was hung, like a discarded coat, on the rack of "God, the creator and maintainer of the Universe."

Beyond Space and Time

But I, like the ancients, feel that the question of origins and the "why" questions *do* belong in the domain of science. If the "why" questions cannot be asked within the framework of our physics, then there must be something dreadfully wrong with that framework.

Gradually, through the growth of scientific knowledge, and its triumph over theology in the domain of physical explanations, it was found that matter does move by itself without the interference of presiding deities. The behavior of matter, under the influence of gravity, shows none of the whims of a god or goddess. It moves according to rigid laws in a way quite unlike the behavior of people or animals. The secret of the behavior of matter lay within matter itself. It was the age of scientific materialism. It was a solid gain, because the old notion of why matter moved was wrong.. The remaining difficulty was that the notion of divine intervention had not been replaced by anything better. The problem of why things moved was still unsolved. We, the

Preface

European physicists, knew how things fell, and it didn't seem to have anything to do with "vital energy," but we still didn't know why they fell. We didn't know why matter showed gravity, electricity and inertia. The framework of our physics was still incomplete.

It wasn't until after the advent of relativity theory, in 1905, that we even had the essential clue which would lead to the unraveling of this problem and to the completion of the framework of our physics. This missing clue, which is only hinted at by relativity theory, had remained hidden in Europe, probably by the conflict between science and the church, but it had been known much earlier, and worked out in some detail, by some of our Asiatic compatriots, namely the Buddhists and the Vedantins. Europe knew how things moved, and Asia knew why, and this book is about the confluence of these two streams of human knowledge. The Buddhists and Vedantins (especially the Shunyavada Buddhists and the Advaita Vedantins[1], who

---

[1] The term Advaita Vedanta is Sanskrit. It means non-dualistic Vedanta. Vedanta, literally, means the culmination

hold that the reality underlying this Universe is non-dual), by quarreling with each other, had worked out the details of why things move (what I call apparitional causation[1]), while the scientists of Europe, quarreling with the church, had worked out the details of how things move (what I call transformational

---

of knowledge. Veda means knowledge, and Anta means end or culmination. The Vedantins hold that all this that we see is Brahman, the one self-existent spirit, the absolute, beyond time, space and causation. Brahman is the real, the eternal truth. What we see within space and time is the transient.

Basically there are two schools of thought among the Vedantins. The dualists hold that Brahman has beome all this through what is called Parinama, transformation. And they hold that even in the final analysis the individual soul is different from Brahman. The Advaitins, the non-dualists (dvaita means dual) on the other hand, hold that Brahman only appears to have become this Universe. They hold that the individual soul, through Maya (apparition), only appears to be different from Brahman, and that in reality there is no differentiation whatsoever.

[1] Apparitional causation is causation by appearance only, as when a rope is mistaken for a snake, or when the stump of a tree is mistaken for a man. The rope is not actually transformed into a snake, as milk may be transformed into buttermilk, or as the gravitational energy of a falling object may be transformed into its kinetic energy during the fall. According to the Advaita Vedantins, the reality (Brahman) has been seen through apparition (Maya) as this visible Universe.

Preface

causation), and had gained a fair understanding of our genetic past. It was the confluence of these two streams of knowledge, the joining of these two "maps," that was needed for the clarification of our problem. What remained unclear at the edge of the map of science was why matter appeared as discrete electrical particles showing gravity and inertia. And what remained unclear at the edge of the map of Vedanta was how the nature of the underlying reality, seen through apparition, would show up in our physics

J.L.D.
October 1, 1979

Acknowledgements

This book, for all its smallness, owes so much to so many that any adequate acknowledgment seems out of the question. "We stand on the shoulders of giants" -- many giants. The debt goes back to many in ancient Greece, to Euclid, and to Democritus who believed in "atoms and the void, and the gravity of atoms." In ancient India, it goes back to the authors of the Upanishads, whose names we don't know. The debt goes back, in more recent times, to such figures as Galileo and Newton, in Europe, and to Shankara, in India. In modern times it goes back to Nikola Tesla, who tried to show that what we call matter is simply potential energy, and to Albert Einstein, who succeeded. On the Asiatic side it goes back to Swami Vivekananda, who posed the problem to Tesla, and to Swami Ashokananda, who posed the problem to me. [1] I should also mention certain other persons whom I had the good fortune to meet, such as Niels Bohr and Werner Heisenberg, and Dr. E. O. Lawrence, under whom I studied at the university. Then there is Erwin Schrodinger, whom I failed to meet. Finally, among persons still living, I must acknowledge my special indebtedness to Sir Fred Hoyle and to Dr. Richard Feynman.

But there is another debt which I feel bound to acknowledge. That is the debt to those who have left mistakes, some large, some small, in their presentation of the material, either in lectures or in their printed works. The great benefit, to me, of these mistakes has been that they forced me to sleuth my way through with a growing distrust of both the spoken and the printed word. And I hope the same distrust will guide the readers of this book. Einstein

---

[1] The task of reconciling Advaita Vedanta with modern science was laid on my head long ago by Swami Ashokananda. The present work was written thirty years later at the request of Swami Swahananda of Hollywood as a series of articles to be published in *Prabuddha Bharata*, an English magazine of the Ramakrishna Order in India.

Acknowledgements

himself, when discussing Mach's principle that inertia here depends on inertia there, suggested that if we took a test particle far from the other matter of the Universe, its rest mass (its inertia) should approach zero. No! It is the separation of the test particle, in the gravitational field, from all the other matter of the Universe that gives it its rest mass, not its proximity. Although the gravitational field strength goes up with proximity, the gravitational energy is related to the space between the particles and goes up with their separation.

Another such mistake, which can be found in almost any physics text, is that the path of a projectile in a gravitational field (overlooking friction, etc.) is a parabola. No! It would be a parabola only if the gravitational field were non-convergent (parallel), but it is a fundamental characteristic of the Universe that gravitational fields are always convergent. That is how one could tell from within Einstein's famous closed box whether that box was being pulled faster and faster with a constant acceleration, or whether it was at rest

Beyond Space and Time

in a gravitational field. If the box were being constantly accelerated, the path of a projectile with respect to the box would be parabolic; but if the box were at rest in a gravitational field, the path would be an ellipse. Although, numerically, the mistake would be minor, conceptually, it is total. Let the reader of the present work beware!

Another such mistake is quite usually made in discussing the geometrical aspect of relativity theory. It is often said that, between two events, where one observer sees more of time and less of space, another observer, moving with respect to the first, would see more of space and less of time. Once again, no! Time is not another dimension of space. The observer who sees the greater space between the two events sees also the greater time. Let the reader beware!

Contents

5

Beyond Space and Time

---

* Title from William Blake's poem "The Tyger."

Illustrations

The concentric circles as in the illustration above are a stylized representation of the diffraction pattern of light through a circular opening. It is used here to symbolize the spread of knowledge. As Sri Krishna says in the Gita, "In this world there is no purifier like knowledge."

The first map (Page 19) symbolizes the spread of Advaita Vedanta and the understanding of "apparitional causation" or Maya from Northwest India during the last few thousand years.

The second map (Page 61) symbolizes the spread of Einstein's notions that revolutionized our understanding of science. The pattern is centered on Bern, Switzerland, where, as a

7

young clerk in the patent office, Einstein published his first paper on relativity theory in 1905.

The third map (Page 121) represents the coming together of these two patterns along the West Coast of North America, and symbolizes the confluence of these two streams of knowledge.

The final illustration (Page 165) represents several hundred millions of years of genetic development, leading to the brain of modern man, but not yet beyond it. The pattern symbolizing the spread of human knowledge is centered on the frontal lobes of the most recent product of this slow genetic development, the future course of which is as yet uncertain.

Introduction

Sri Ramakrishna was born in 1836 in an obscure village of Bengal. His story is too well known to be repeated here. He came, he practiced all sorts of spiritual practices, had innumerable spiritual experiences, saw the reality from many points of view and, in 1886, he passed away, leaving behind a small band of disciples in the trusted hands of Narendra Nath whom we have come to know as Swami Vivekananda. To Swamiji fell the task of trying to interpret that life to the world at large. His was the vision that that life was not a private life but had been lived for all mankind and must somehow be understood and interpreted. Against what philosophical backdrop could the experiences of that life best be viewed? Against what map could the journeys of that life best be traced?

Beyond Space and Time

A philosophy, like a map or a system of physics, is either true or false according as it corresponds or does not correspond to fact. This question does not arise with respect to religions. A religion is simply a path, and about a path one does not ask whether it is true or false but only, "Will it take me to the goal?" Sri Ramakrishna showed in his own life that innumerable religious practices, courses of Sadhana in great profusion, lead to the same goal. Swamiji's task was to find a philosophical backdrop against which we could best understand that fact, and against which we could best understand the tremendous renunciation of that life.

Swami Vivekananda saw that the philosophy of Advaita Vedanta made the best fit with the experiences and teachings of Sri Ramakrishna. Not that each of Sri Ramakrishna's teachings can be taken as pointing directly to Advaita. Not at all. He spoke to many people from many points of view. But what Swamiji saw was that in scaling the heights of spiritual realization,

Introduction

many vistas unfold themselves before the eyes of the climber. The reality is one, but the views are many. The mountain may be one, but the trails are many. What is the nature of the reality that underlies these sublime vistas? And what is the nature of the screen through which we see it which accounts for the proliferation of our points of view and our descriptions?

Swamiji saw that the nature of the reality (Brahman) and the nature of the screen (Maya) as described by the Advaita Vedantins constituted our best map -- our best philosophical backdrop. But when we study the sayings of Sri Ramakrishna, we do not find him recommending what is usually understood as the practice of Advaita Vedanta. Rather, we find him cautioning his listeners that so long as one has body consciousness one should not say "I am He." It is in spite of these cautions that we find Swamiji teaching Advaita Vedanta broadcast not only all over India but in America and Europe as well, because he saw that except on the basis of Advaita Vedanta it would be impossible for us to understand the beauty and significance of Sri Ramakrishna's life.

Clarity, at this point, demands a sharp discrimination between Advaita Vedanta as a map and the practices which naturally follow from an understanding of that map. To understand that the nature of the reality is one and undivided and that our sense of separation between the perceiver and the perceived is simply an apparition arising through the Gunas, is to understand Advaita Vedanta as a map. Constantly to meditate in the mind that the perceiver is real and the perceived is nothing is simply one of several practices which naturally follow from an understanding of that map. We call it, "I, I monism." This practice is embodied in the refrain of Shankara's Nirvanashatakam, "Chidananda rupah Shivoham, Shivoham." (I am of the nature of consciousness-bliss, I am Shiva, I am Shiva.") But when Sri Ramakrishna heard this refrain he would quietly add at the end "Tuhu, Tuhu." ("Thou, Thou.") We call this "Thou, Thou monism." Constantly to meditate in the mind that Thou art all is as much a practice of

12

Introduction

monism as the other and follows from the same map. Likewise, Swamiji's worship of Daridra Narayana follows from the same map. "All this is Brahman." It was Advaita Vedanta as a map that Swamiji taught. He was not so fussy about which road one chose. The map is one, but the roads are many. Girish Chandra Ghosh said that Mahamaya could not catch two souls, Nag Mahashaya and Swami Vivekananda. She didn't have a net big enough to hold Swamiji nor one with a fine enough mesh to catch Nag.

WESTERNERS THINK SCIENCE

Teaching in what we call the West, that is in America and Europe, Swamiji had a special problem -- how to present the map against the cultural background of his listeners. Westerners think science. In Europe and America people think and act against the background of science. Science is their map. They do not think and act against the background of philosophy as people do in India. For thousands of years the Indian mind has lived and thought philosophy. In India

Beyond Space and Time

Swamiji found a language ready-made for handling philosophical ideas. There is no language on the face of the earth even comparable to Sanskrit in its competence to handle philosophical concepts. Swamiji found himself translating and re-translating from Sanskrit to English. In English there is no word for Vivartavada (the doctrine that the first cause is apparitional). Parinama (transformation) is understood but not Vivarta. There is no word for Brahman, for Atman, for Maya or for the Gunas. It is not just that the words are absent; the ideas are also absent.

THE FIVE ELEMENTS

In the West Swamiji found it necessary to connect his map of Advaita Vedanta with the map of European science. (I have avoided the term "modern science," which is the term Swamiji would have used, because what we now call modern science was not yet born. It is an important point, and I shall return to it.) It was clear to Swamiji, as it should be to anyone, that when the Vedantic cosmologists spoke of the Panchamahabhutas (the five great

Introduction

elements), perceivable by our five senses of perception, they were talking physics. And Swamiji tried again and again to translate the terms Akasha, Vayu, Tejas, Ap and Prithivi to English. Again and again he failed, partly because of the inadequacy of the science of his day. It is easy, now, to translate those terms to English, as we shall subsequently show.

CLASSICAL PHYSICS

The important point to note here is that the physics of Swamiji's day could never have been squared with Advaita Vedanta. The physics wasn't ready. The physics of Swamiji's day was what we now call "classical physics." It was the physics of real particles with real mass and real energy moving through real space in real time. It was the map that underlay the materialistic worldview of Victorian England. It was the physics of Newtonian mechanics and Euclidean geometry, and it was the crowning glory of centuries of careful investigation. That physics was free of all internal inconsistencies, and it had only one defect. It did not correspond to fact. At every step the physicist must ask the real world if his physics is true, and by the end of the last century it was becoming clearer and clearer that the answer was no.

MODERN PHYSICS

What we now call modern science, or more properly modern physics, can be said to have been born in 1905 with the publication of two papers by Albert Einstein. From those two papers there gradually arose a completely new understanding of the nature of the reality which underlies the map of Western science. Slowly the map has changed. Classical physics has given way to relativity theory and quantum mechanics. Our old notions of time, space and causation were wrong. The new map, based on relativity theory and quantum mechanics, arose from a new understanding of the relation of space to time and from a new understanding of causation -- a new understanding of the nature of the necessary interaction, in physical measurement, between the perceiver and the perceived, or rather, between the instrument of perception and the

Introduction

thing perceived. From this new understanding has come a sea change in our physics on the basis of which it is now easy to square it with Advaita Vedanta. Swamiji said that science and religion would meet and shake hands. That time has come.

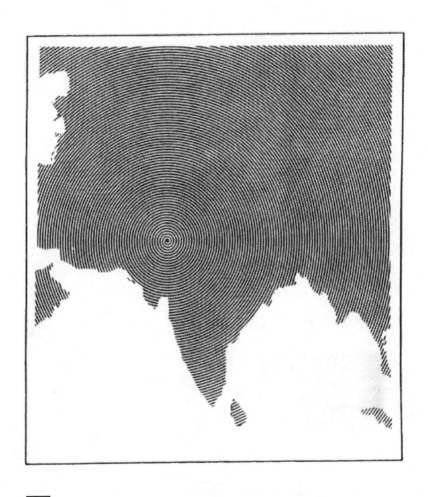

| I | The map of Advaita Vedanta

The Gunas and Causation

A lecture delivered in Hollywood to the Vedanta Society of Southern California, Sunday, December 10, 1978.

Let me begin with a quote from Plutarch:

"All becoming has two causes, of which the most ancient theologians and poets chose to turn their attention to the stronger only, pronouncing over all things the universal refrain: "Zeus first, Zeus middle, all things Zeus," while they never approached the necessary or physical causes. Their successors, called Physikoi (the physicists), did the very reverse; they strayed away from the beautiful and divine principle and refer all things to bodies, and impacts, and changes, and combinations."

I want to talk about both kinds of causation. Swami Ashokananda once said that Vedanta is like a great department store. There are all sorts of items for sale there, items to suit almost every need. You go; you buy what you need. It is not required that you buy everything in the store. But there are certain things that have been, in my opinion,

21

dishonestly advertised, and I feel that the shelf displays need some touching up, and among those items which have been wrongly represented are the three Gunas and the Five Elements. But first I need to present the problem.

THE PROBLEM

Suppose we just consider the present situation. You see somebody here, an embodied being, moving and talking, and the question is: Of what are these bodies made? Of what is all this made? Well, the chemists will give you a real quick answer. They are made of a very few ingredients. There are only about 92 things out of which this visible world is made, and these bodies are made of only a handful of those 92. Really not an awful lot of things; hydrogen and oxygen and carbon and nitrogen and a few other things in smaller amounts. Now where do they come from? They come from the stars. That is to say, all except hydrogen are derived from hydrogen in the bellies of stars. Hydrogen falls together by gravity in a star like our Sun – well, let's take a larger star, not one like our Sun. Let's consider a larger star because the other chemical elements that get scattered around here, out of which these bodies are made, are not made in stars like our Sun. Our Sun will make helium out of hydrogen, and carbon and oxygen out of helium, and that's probably as far as it will go. But larger stars make a whole lot of other things, larger chemical nuclei up to the size of iron, and when the centers of those stars are iron, those centers collapse by gravity and the outer portions are blown away by the energy released in the collapse.

FROM HYDROGEN

Out of those things we are made; that is to say, out of those things our bodies are made, and all of those things were made out of hydrogen by what we call transformational causation. The hydrogen goes to helium, the helium goes to carbon, the carbon goes to oxygen then to neon, magnesium, and so forth, and all of this is transformational causation, and we understand it very well. It is governed by the conservation laws; for example, in any transformation, the energy at the end is never more than the energy at the beginning.

But the hydrogen does not arise by transformational causation. It cannot arise by transformational causation. Hydrogen is made of energy, and energy cannot arise by the transformation of energy. Hydrogen is made of electrical particles, and those particles do not arise by the transformation of something else. The electrical particles fall together by gravity, and the gravity does not arise by transformational causation. And the electrical particles have inertia, and the inertia does not arise by transformational causation.

WHENCE HYDROGEN?

Now this, really, is the big problem in human knowledge. We have understood for a long time how transformational causation goes. We start with certain ingredients and end up with something else. The Sun begins as hydrogen and ends up as carbon and oxygen. The great question is: How do the *original* ingredients arise?

The Gunas and Causation

Now instead of taking the materials out of which all this is made, let's take the energies. It's obvious that I'm moving around, and my lips are moving. All this is done on some kind of energy. And when we look at the kind of energy, we find that it is chemical energy. It comes from eating. There's a story on that. Swami Shantaswarupananda, when he first came to this country, wouldn't eat well. He just ate the teeniest amounts, like Swami Pavitrananda, and I was supposed to feed him you see, and to see that his diet was properly nutritious, but he wouldn't eat it. And so, Swami Ashokananda was upstairs to scold him one day and said, "All energy comes from food. Spiritual energy also comes from food. The more you eat, the more spiritual you are." (Laughter)

ENERGY FROM SUNLIGHT

Well, this energy by which we move these bodies around is actually canned sunlight. It is chemical energy now. We get it by eating potatoes and wheat grains and corn and various other things and by drinking milk and by eating cows and chickens and various things, but the energy that they have comes from the Sun. The energy changes from one form to another without any change in the amount. The plants hold out their hands and catch the sunlight. They pick up carbon dioxide with their hands, and water with their feet, and there are a few minerals thrown in, but that's not where the energy comes from. The energy comes from the Sun. So when we eat all those things, we oxidize them back to carbon dioxide and water. When the plants got them they were carbon dioxide, water and sunlight. After we're through with them, they're once again carbon dioxide and water, and we run around on the canned sunlight.

So all this that you see moving here is moving on canned sunlight. Even these lights that burn here are burning on canned sunlight. The Sun puts water up into the sky, we catch it in the mountains, run it down through those big turbines, and we cause the electrons to flow through these wires. But it's canned sunlight. Now where does the Sun get its energy?

The Gunas and Causation

Now you see, we are tracing it back. We're tracing it back to its source. It's chemical energy here, that's electromagnetic energy. But formerly it was radiational energy coming from the Sun. Before that it was kinetic energy in the Sun. The energy that the Sun radiates away, in the state before it is radiated away, is kinetic energy. But how did the Sun get its kinetic energy? How did it get so hot? It got hot by falling together by gravity. Now, once again, this is all transformational causation. We start with certain ingredients and end up with something else, something which looks very different, not by any change in the amount of energy but only by a change in form. From gravitational energy it goes to kinetic energy then to radiation then to electrical and magnetic energy and we move around. All this is transformational causation. The energy changes in form but not in amount, and these other forms of energy come from gravitational energy by this transformation. But the gravitational energy does not arise by transformation. Now there is the problem, you

27

see. All the chemical elements besides hydrogen arise from hydrogen by this kind of causation, and all these other energies arise from gravitational energy by this kind of causation, but neither the hydrogen nor its gravitational energy can arise in that way.

WHENCE THE FIVE ELEMENTS?

Now these five kinds of energy that I just listed are the Five Great Elements of antiquity, and they need to be properly dusted off and re-translated into English.* The present

---

* *Akasha*, usually translated as ether, is the gravitational energy of matter dispersed in space. The word also means space. The gravitational energy is in the space of the dispersion. Our orientation in the gravitational field is perceived, through the saccule in the ear.
Vayu, usually translated as air, is kinetic energy. As matter, dispersed in space, falls together by gravity, the gravitational energy is converted to kinetic energy. Kinetic energy is perceived as temperature, through the skin.
Tejas, usually translated as fire, is radiation. The word means that which shines. The excess kinetic energy (heat energy) of a condensing star is lost to the surrounding space as the energy of its radiation. It is radiation which is perceived through the eye.
Ap and *Prithivi*, usually translated as water and earth, are electricity and magnetism. The presiding deities of Ap and Prithivi were said to be twins. Electricity and magnetism go together. You cannot have one without the other. Electricity and magnetism are perceived through the tongue and the nose.

translation, which is probably in all the books on these premises, including the Sanskrit dictionary, has Akasha translated as ether. But the notion of ether left physics in 1905, and it is high time somebody noticed that and redid the translation. Ether will not do. There is no such animal. Now to translate that fine Sanskrit word as ether is, in my opinion, dishonest advertising. And if we are to be honest, in this department store of Vedanta, we should advertise the wares satisfactorily.

Now the notion that there are five great forms of energy is an old, old idea. In the Upanishads we find the statement that "From Brahman arises Akasha. From Akasha arises Vayu. From Vayu arises Tejas. From Tejas arises Ap and from Ap arises Prithivi." These are the Five Great Elements of antiquity, usually translated ether, air, fire, water and earth. You may skip all those translations. The first energy is gravitational energy. It goes to kinetic energy, that goes to radiation and that goes to electricity and magnetism, which were

---

Protons taste sour, and the molecular configurations perceived through the nose are magnetic.

said to be twins. They really are twins. Those
people had it straight – very, very straight –
and a very long time ago.

GRAVITY, NOT SOUND

Now those five energies are said to be
perceived by our five senses. Akasha is said to
be perceived by the ear. The ear has three
kinds of sensations and the oldest one, the
saccule, senses our orientation in the
gravitational field. Now in all your books, the
first element will be translated as sound. But
the Universe does not arise from sound. Not
only that, but sound arises by transformation
and not by the first cause, or Prakriti. By the
first cause (from Brahman) Akasha arises. It is
gravitational energy. From that arises an
energy, Vayu, which is perceivable by the skin.
That is kinetic energy. Temperature is a
measure of kinetic energy. From that arises
Tejas, "that which shines." It doesn't mean
fire, it means that which shines. It means
radiation, some of which is perceivable by the
eyes. From that arises Ap and Prithivi,
electricity and magnetism, perceivable by the

tongue and the nose. Protons taste sour. The raw ingredients of this Universe, that is to say the heavy ones, the protons, the nuclei of the hydrogen atoms, taste sour. Nothing else in this Universe tastes sour. So electricity is what we taste with the tongue. The nose perceives molecular configurations, and that's a magnetic problem. That's complicated and I'm not going to go into it, but the magnetic pairing of the electrons is what holds the molecules together; so the structures are really magnetic structures and those structures we perceive by the nose.

HYDROGEN AND GRAVITY

Now you see this is really our problem. We can trace the material of these bodies and the materials of all this stuff that we see with our eyes back to hydrogen. It is perfectly easy; we know all the details now. But we have no way to get the hydrogen, the original material. It cannot arise by transformational causation. And we can trace all these energies back to the energy of gravitation, electricity and nuclear energy, but we have no origin for energy. We have no origin for the electrical particles which make up the hydrogen, no origin for energy and no origin for inertia.

THE FIRST CAUSE

Now this problem, the problem of the first cause, was handled a long, long time ago by some physicists in Northern India, probably some 5,000 years ago. Probably somewhere between 2,000 and 3,000 B.C. these things were thought out very carefully in North India – but not by the Aryans. We think, you see, when we think of India, that it has been inhabited by Aryans all along. That's not so. This was done probably by the people who planted rice. Now the rice people, the people who invented the planting of rice, were in India long before the Aryans came, and there is another batch of people called the Pre-Aryans. They also came before the Aryans. So these old, old people, the Proto-Australoids, probably Rama's people, were there some time around 3,000 B.C. planting rice, and apparently they invented this worship which we do with five ingredients – not the Aryans. It was much older than that, and they apparently discussed these different kinds of energies and noticed that there are five different kinds associated with our five senses of perception. It is perfectly straight physics, perfectly straight astronomy. There's only one other kind of energy that we talk about in this Universe and that is nuclear energy. That has to do with the electrical rearrangement of the particles in the nucleus. It has to do with the uncertainty principle. Ordinary energies are five, and we do perceive them with our five senses. Not only do *we* perceive them. Even one-celled organisms perceive them, and the atoms themselves perceive them, that is, the atoms themselves respond to these same five forms of energy. There's no use saying, suppose we had another sense then the Universe would appear differently – no, we have the right number now. That's all the energies there are to see. We don't have to fool around with more dimensions, either. That's not the problem. The problem is to understand how this hydrogen arises, and it does *not* arise by transformational causation.

Beyond Space and Time

OLD SANSKRIT

Now the notions that are current in the minds of a people when their language becomes codified get embodied in the language, and Sanskrit was codified in India. It comes from that line of languages called the Indo-European languages, related to Greek and Latin and a whole lot of other languages, but Sanskrit was codified in India. The reason we know that is because of the animals that are associated with the early language. When you hear about peacocks and tigers you understand that you are in Bengal. You're not in Greece; they didn't have peacocks. (Laughter) It's the same as Little Black Sambo. You see, when I was a boy, I thought that Little Black Sambo was an African boy. It wasn't until I was quite grown up that I noticed that he was associated with tigers and melted butter. Now tigers and melted butter are in India and Little Black Sambo is little black Shambhu. Shambhu is a name of Shiva, and it is not an African story at any time. You see I had to be quite grown up to notice this. We take things for granted. Now we know that the Sanskrit language was

The Gunas and Causation

codified in India, and in that language we now have those ideas from the Proto-Australoids who grew rice and did all these worships and studied the Five Elements and all those interesting things.

THEIR UNDERSTANDING

What happened, apparently, was that the Aryans entered India, probably some time around 2,000 B.C., gradually fell deeply in love with what they found there when they came, put it into Sanskrit, and by diligent efforts of memory lasting several thousand years, they have passed it down to us. Some of it has been passed down so long that the meanings have been lost. For example, the entire Indian nation thinks that this Universe arises from sound. But that is wrong. They've even designated the sound: It's Aum. But the energies of this Universe do not arise from sound. Sound arises by transformation. The energies of this Universe are first gravitation, electricity and nuclear energy, then kinetic energy and radiation.

Beyond Space and Time

And the important point to notice is this – that the first cause, which we are here to discuss, gives rise to gravitational energy. That is, as the Upanishad says, "From Brahman arises Akasha." Kinetic energy arises by transformation. But from Brahman to Akasha cannot be by transformation. Now those old notions were put into Sanskrit and passed down to us largely in the form of the Upanishads. There may be some older texts but mostly these things are passed down in the Upanishads. And later on, people had to see if they could systematize the teachings of the Upanishads, and that's where these famous six systems of philosophy arose – Sankhya and Yoga, Vaisheshika and Nyaya, Purva Mimamsa and Uttara Mimamsa or Vedanta. All these things arose in an effort to put the teachings of the Upanishads in order. Those books are very disorderly. They consist of the blurtings of people who saw things – that's all. "Na tatra suryo bhati na chandra tarakam ..." "Not there the Sun shines nor Moon nor star. There the lightening does not flash, how could

36

The Gunas and Causation

this fire!" – like that. They are just simply sudden statements of somebody seeing something. "Those who know the high Brahman, the Vast, hidden in the bodies of all creatures and alone enveloping everything as the Lord, they become immortal. I know that great Purusha of sun-like lustre beyond the darkness. A man who knows Him truly passes over death, there is no other path to go." It does not sound like a school book. Nobody sat down there and tried to organize this stuff. They simply saw things, experienced things, and let them come out through the mouth, and somebody heard it and memorized it. Somebody heard it and, fortunately for us, memorized it and taught it to their children, and their children, and their children, for several thousands years. Now we have them printed up. They're not in such danger of being lost. But whole hosts of those things got lost. Probably we have saved not more than a few percent of those things that those old physicists, the Rishis, said. We don't even know who they were. We know something about what they saw and what they said.

Beyond Space and Time

SANKHYA AND THE GUNAS

Now Sankhya is considered to be the first systemization of those Upanishads, of the thoughts that have been passed down in the Upanishads. But the Sankhyans taught entirely transformational causation. They did not have the basic understanding by which they could even understand the language of the Upanishads. I don't like to insult people like this, but it is a very important point. We are here talking about Gunas, and the whole notion of the Gunas is completely disconnected from transformational causation. It is probably wrong to think that the Sankhyans used the Gunas first. They occur in the Upanishads, and in their proper context, but in Sankhya they think of the Gunas as *things* and they do chemistry with them. A little bit of this and a little bit of that and we'll make something. No! That is not what the Gunas are about. The Gunas are about some entirely different kind of causation.

THE SANKHYAN IDEA OF THE FIRST CAUSE

Now the Sankhyans say that Prakriti is the first cause. The word means first cause. It

The Gunas and Causation

comes from Pra, first, and Kri, to do. And they say that the first cause is made of three Gunas.

So far, they're perfectly right. But what is the nature of this first cause? By what kind of causation can you get from Brahman to hydrogen dispersed in space and falling together in its gravitational field? You see, it is really a very hard thing to understand. From a completely formless, completely changeless, infinite, undivided Brahman, you get what we see. Quite a bit divided – divided into atoms. Quite a bit finite – teeny, weenie electrical particles. And quite a bit active – falling together by gravity into galaxies and stars.

THE FIRST CAUSE
THAT IS NOT IN SPACE AND TIME

Now you see, when we say that Brahman is changeless, we say it because we see things in time. And what we mean is that Brahman is not in time. And when we say that Brahman is infinite, we mean that it's not in space. What we see is in space. Now this business of seeing things in space and time is wrong. We know it now from our physics.

Beyond Space and Time

EINSTEIN'S GEOMETRY

Since 1905 we have gradually come to understand, even from our physics, that the notion of seeing things away from us in space and backwards in time is wrong. The Universe appears in such a way that we see the whole thing in the past. We cannot see anything when it happens. It is only by seeing events late that we are able to see them away from us.

The equation of separation in Einstein's relativity theory puts the separation between the perceiver and the perceived at zero. We see events away from us in space by a trick – we see them backwards in time. And if you're talking about an event of your perception, and the event that that event perceives, then the separation between those two events is zero. Suppose you see a flash of light from a star. We'll call that an event. And your perception of that event we'll call the second event. The separation between those two events is zero. If you can see the event there-then from the event here-now then the separation between those two events is zero, because in that case, always, the distance away is exactly balanced by the time in the past. And because space and time are opposites, if the distance away is exactly equal to the time in the past, the total separation is zero.

OPPOSITES

If the money you put into the bank is exactly equal to the money which you take out of bank, then the change in your bank balance is zero. If the number of positive electrical charges which you have in a box is exactly balanced by the number of negative electrical charges which you have in that same box, then the total electrical charge on that box is zero.

That's what we mean by opposites, two things that are identical and yet in some sense opposite, so that if you have the same amount of both, it's like having none of either. Now space and time are opposites in that sense. They're both dimensions, and they both come into the equation of separation.

PERCEPTION

Relativity theory has pointed out in completely unambiguous terms that a distance in space is not a real thing. It's not objective.

Beyond Space and Time

People disagree on distances in space according to how fast they're going by. And lengths of time are also not objective. There's no such thing as an hour. What you call an hour and what an astronaut flying by in a spaceship at a speed close to the speed of light will call an hour are very different things.

What relativity theory pointed out is that it's the combination of space and time which has some semblance of objectivity. If you want to see the Universe as objective, that is to say, as independent of the observers, then you must see it in four dimensions- three dimensions of space (right and left, front and back, up and down, perpendicular to each other) and one dimension of time. Now the equations say that space and time are opposites in that very interesting sense; so that between two events, say between here-now and there-then, if the distance between here and there is equal to the time between now and then, then the total separation between the event here-now and the event there-then is zero. It's a very important point because every event that you see, you see as away from you in space and backwards in time, and in every instance the distance is equal to the time, so that the total separation, the four-dimensional separation, the objective separation, between the perceiver and the perceived goes to zero.

WHAT IS BEYOND SPACE AND TIME

Now if we ask what is behind this, if we ask, from our physics, what is behind what we see, then it says right away that what is behind it is beyond space and time. That is what we mean when we say undivided, infinite and changeless. Undivided means that it couldn't be in space. With space you can see things as divided. Without space you cannot see them as divided. With space you can see things as small. Without space you cannot see them as small. With time you can see things as changing. Without time you cannot see things as changing. Now when we say that the nature of the reality is infinite, we don't mean that it's bigger than space. (Laughter) We mean that it has nothing to do with space. Space is simply a mistake in our perception. And when we say that the nature of the reality is eternal, we don't mean that it lasts longer than time. What we mean is that the reality is completely devoid of our concepts of space and time. So when we go to describe the reality, Brahman, we find it is totally indescribable, so we grope. From the standpoint of space and time we point the finger. We say if it's beyond space it's undivided. If it's beyond space it's infinite. And if it's beyond time it's changeless. That much description of Brahman we can get from physics – that what is behind this Universe of physics is changeless, infinite and undivided.

MATTER?

Now we see it as divided – very finely divided into atoms – and nobody ever understood why. And we see it squeezed down to these minute electrical particles and nobody ever understood why. Einstein said, "We cannot understand on theoretical grounds why matter should appear as discrete electrical particles." And we see this thing as changing, and, once again, no one ever understood why. By no one, here, I mean no modern physicist has ever understood why what we see should be divided into atoms, made of discrete electrical particles, moving, falling together by gravity, and yet resisting every change in its state of motion. You see how crazy it is. It wants to fall together by gravity, it wants to fly apart by electricity, and it wants to remain totally stationary. (Laughter) Well, you laugh, but you're no different. We do exactly the same thing. We want to be totally in love, totally free, and totally alone. (Laughter) We fall in love; we get married. Then we find that our freedom is gone, and we want out. And once again we're lonely. And we want in, and we get out, and all the time we say, "Leave me alone!"

The Universe is made out of frustration. There is nothing accidental about it. It is made out of frustration because we see the Universe by a mistake. We see it as in space and time by a trick – by a mistake.

THE MISTAKE

Now those old people, either the Mohenjo-Daro people or, more likely, the earlier Proto-Australoids, probably had this figured out. We don't know how long ago it was figured out that this whole thing is seen by a mistake. The kind of causation by which we see this thing is a causation by mistake – what we call apparitional causation – the kind of thing that you do when you mistake a rope for a snake. Nothing happens to the rope. But when you mistake a rope for a snake, three things are necessary. First, you fail to see the rope rightly. This is the veiling power of Tamas. Secondly, you see the rope as something *else*. Now this else business is the projecting power of Rajas. And then, thirdly, you saw the rope in the first place, otherwise you could not have mistaken it for a snake. You didn't mistake some other thing for the snake. You mistook the rope for the snake, because you saw the rope. This is the revealing power of Sattva. The mistake is not made at midnight and it is not made at noon. In the Sanskrit books it is specified that it is done in the twilight, as probably you are all aware. Why? Because you do have to see the rope, but you mustn't see it rightly.

The Gunas and Causation

Now the veiling power of Tamas, the projecting power of Rajas, and the revealing power of Sattva – that is where the notion of the Gunas arises, in connection with the first cause, Prakriti, or Maya. The Vedantins say that Maya is made of three Gunas. The Sankhyans say that Prakriti, the first cause, is made of three Gunas. But the notion of the three Gunas arises here, and not in transformational causation.

Sankhya took the whole thing the wrong way. They went all the way down through their entire cosmology building everything out of the Gunas. *Nothing* is built out of a Guna. Nowadays you find in most of the Sanskrit literature that Rajas is activity. No. There is no mention in the Sanskrit dictionary of any activity in relation to Rajas. It is an impurity, the notion of an impurity, like smog. If you're talking about the sky, smog is there, that is Rajas. If you're talking about a field and it's all grown with grass that's fine, but if you plow it and make it all dusty that has to do with Rajas. If you have nice, clear water that's fine, but if

47

you put something in it, that's Rajas. It's an impurity. It's seeing something *else*. I even hear such extravagant notions as matter is Tamas, energy is Rajas and consciousness is Sattva. Erase! Erase! No such animal. Matter is made out of energy. Matter is energy. We learned that from relativity theory. There are not two different things called matter and energy. It is just, once again, a mistake in our perception.

VEILING, PROJECTING AND REVEALING

So there's no use trying to use the Gunas for things like that. The Gunas arise in apparitional causation. When you mistake one thing for another, you fail to see the thing rightly because of the veiling power of Tamas. You jump to a wrong conclusion because of the projection power of Rajas. But first of all you did see the thing, by the revealing power of Sattva. For instance, if you mistake a rope for a snake, you do see the length and diameter of the rope, but you see it as the length and diameter of a snake.

The Gunas and Causation

Now the curious thing is this, that if you mistake the changeless, the infinite, the undivided for the changing, the finite and divided, you had to see the changeless, the infinite, the undivided first, last and always. Because really there is nothing else to see. And the changeless, the infinite, the undivided has to show up in our hydrogen, just as the length and diameter of the rope must show up in the snake. If you see the reality as divided into atoms, the atoms will all come back together like a stretched rubber band, by gravity. Gravity is the undividedness seen in the divided. Electricity is the infinitude seen in the finite. Inertia is that changelessness seen in the changing. The more squeezed down into tiny electrical particles you see it, the more electrical energy those particles will have. The more spaced out those particles appear, the more gravitational energy those particles will have. And finally, the faster you see the particles moving, the more inertia they will appear to have.

49

Beyond Space and Time

Now this is what the Universe consists of. We see it as divided into atoms, but falling together by gravity. The undividedness has been seen. We see this as made of minute particles, and yet every one of them is electrical; it wants to become infinite. As Swami Vivekananda said, "The whole Universe is not big enough for even one particle." Everything tends toward infinite dispersion. Everything tends toward infinite condensation, and everything tends to resist every change in its state of motion.

Now everything in the Universe runs toward the changeless, toward the infinite, toward the undivided. There are no other goals. There is no mechanical Universe driven from behind. No. The whole thing is driven from the front. Hydrogen is driven *toward* all other hydrogen in the Universe because the reality is undivided. The electrical particles are driven *toward* infinite expansion because the reality is infinite. And all matter is driven *toward* resisting every change in its state of motion because the reality is changeless.

The Gunas and Causation

Now hydrogen atoms are very direct. If you let them go, they'll fall straight toward the closest blob of matter – no fooling around. (Not that anything comes of it. Nothing reaches the goal through transformational causation.) But unlike the hydrogen, we are indirect. We have egos which are genetically invented and genetically misprogrammed to run in roundabout ways. We run after the undivided, the infinite and the changeless, not by directly falling to the ground and such things, but instead we run at the dictates of the genes to undertake transformational actions – actions by transformational causation – to do the bidding of the genes. That is, we do actions which give rise to viable offspring. We are programmed that way. The whole notion that this is a building and these are lamps – these are genetic notions. Our ego itself is genetic, and the programming of the ego is genetic. We are identified with a piece of matter called the body, and the whole thing goes on from there. But you see, it is not possible to get anything out of it.

Beyond Space and Time

THE MISTAKE IS MADE OUT OF FRUSTRATION

It's made out of frustration, and you can never get anything out of it. If we had gotten into this dilemma by transformational causation, we could get out by transformational causation. If we had gotten into this by walking too slowly, we could get out by walking a little faster. We didn't get in by walking. If we'd gotten into this by talking naughty things, we could get out of it by sweet talk. We didn't get into this by talking. We didn't get into this by any action whatsoever. All actions are transformational in nature and they arise only within the domain of the apparition.

NO

Now this kind of causation that we're talking about now, this apparitional causation, is called, in Sanskrit, *Vivarta*. That means you mistook one thing for another. Nothing has happened. You're still perfectly good. Nothing has happened. The other kind of causation which we've been talking about, transformational causation, is called in Sanskrit, *Parinama*. Now the Sankhyans were

The Gunas and Causation

Parinama-vadins; they believed in transformational causation. The Advaita Vedantins are Vivarta-vadins. They believe that the first cause is apparitional. After that, you can do whatever you like. (Laughter) But the first cause is apparitional. Nothing has happened. Nothing whatsoever. That's why Advaita Vedanta has this notion of *Ajatavada*, complete non-birth. No birth has happened. Nothing has happened.

COUNTER-CHEATING THE GENES

Now you see the problem. Since we are genetically programmed, the problem is to counter-cheat the genes. The genes have us programmed to run after the undivided in a way which will never bear fruit. It bears offspring, but it will never get you to the undivided. The genes have us programmed to run toward these three goals through transformational causation, and the whole thing is just as frustrating as trying to pick yourself up by your bootstraps. You'll never get it done, you see. The whole Universe is like that. We are programmed to run in wrong directions. You see even the hydrogen can't get it, and it's not even misprogrammed. But through space and time, by transformational causation, it is not possible to reach that which is beyond space and time.

SADHANA

So our problem is to counter-cheat the genes. Essentially there are two ways. Either re-direct the genes or tell them to go to blazes. Just don't cooperate. Just tell them to go *to...*, and simply discriminate between the real and the transient. You remember the Vedantins say that there are four things that you have to have if you're going to succeed. "Nityanitya vastu viveka," discrimination between the real and the transient. "Ihamutrartha phalabhogaviraga," renunciation of the enjoyment of the fruits of action. Then there are the six treasures and, finally, Mumukshutvam, or the yearning for liberation. "Ihamutrartha phalabhogaviraga," renunciation of the fruits of action. You see what that means? Don't get caught in transformational causation! Fruits of action

The Gunas and Causation

means you did something by transformational causation and you want something back. You wait for the mailman. (Laughter) You wrote a letter and now you wait for the mailman. Don't wait for the mailman! If you don't expect anything, you're out. It's nice and simple. We sit around here waiting for mailmen. Okay? That's what the game is. You do something and wait for the fruits. So "Ihamutrartha phalabhogaviraga" means, don't wait for any fruits. That's what keeps you here. Expectation keeps you here. Nothing else keeps you here. We've got the wool pulled over our own eyes and we hang onto it tightly.

WHAT TO DO

Someone would have to cut off our hands to get the wool off our eyes, we hang onto it so tightly. So there are four things. First, discrimination between the real and the unreal. We got into it by an indiscrimination, we get out by discrimination, not by action. Second, we have to give up the notion that we're going to get out by action. You see, we have mistaken the rope for the snake and become snake fanciers. First is to discriminate between the rope and the snake. Second is to cease being snake fanciers. Then the next problem is the mind. It's going to be done by the mind. It's not going to be done by somebody else, like your hands or your feet. So you have to have the mind in good shape. Therefore, the third is these "six treasures." You've got to be able to control your senses, and keep them under control, you've got to be able to put up with heat and cold and the faults of others – all these things – and you have to have Shraddha, this tremendous enthusiasm that you're going to get the job done. It's translated as faith, but faith is not a very good translation of Shraddha. It means a tremendous spiritual enthusiasm that you're going to get the job done *now*. Fourth, and finally, you have to have Mumukshutvam. That is to say, yearning for liberation. Now if you look carefully, you'll find that these four things are your four Yogas.

The Gunas and Causation

Jnana Yoga is the discrimination between the real and the unreal. Karma Yoga is doing your actions in such a way that you don't wait for the mailman. Raja Yoga is control of the mind – that's your instrument, that's the boat in which you're going to cross the sea; keep it caulked. And Mumukshutvam, yearning for the reality, that's Bhakti Yoga. You see, it doesn't matter how you look at this, they're always saying the same thing. Whether they speak of these four things that you have to do as part of Jnana Yoga, or whether they speak of the four Yogas, you see that all the four Yogas are there. It doesn't matter, you see, what way you look at it, we got into this by an indiscrimination; we'll get out by discrimination.

Now in Bhakti Yoga what we do is to counter-cheat the genes. If you like to pick flowers, you don't pick them for corsages. You offer them in the worship. If you like to cook, you offer it in the worship. All of the things that you do, you offer in the worship. You see, that is counter-cheating the genes. Worship, rightly done, is simply a counter-cheating device for channeling your actions toward discrimination. The actions which you do in the worship couldn't possibly bear fruit. The genes have us persuaded to run after things through transformational causation. Your trick is to counter-cheat back and do those same actions that are dictated by the genes in such a way that they do not get the genetic job done but contribute, instead, toward your discrimination.

GO BEYOND THE APPARITION

Well. What else is there more to say? If we had gotten into this by transformation, we could get out by transformation. We got in by apparition, we'll get out by undoing the apparition. But this notion of the Gunas, you see, arises there. It would never have arisen in transformational causation. So if, by any chance, you think, or sometimes read, that the Sankhyans invented the notion of the Gunas – no. They not only did not invent the notion of the Gunas – they never had a handle on it. It's the Advaita Vedantins that have it.

The Gunas and Causation

Now I myself am very fond of cartography. I myself feel that if I'm told how I got into this, I'll know what to do about it. I like to know how I got where I am. Once there was a lady in a store, and she asked the clerk if he could please help her out. And he said, "Certainly, Madam, how did you get in?" (Laughter) If you tell me how you got in, I'll tell you how to get out. But we have to understand, you see, that through transformational causation we didn't get in, we don't get out. Now not only is there no action by which you could get out, there's also no action by which you could get in. One place in the Upanishads it says, about a man of realization, "Such thoughts certainly do not distress him, why I did not do the right, why I did what is sinful." In another place it says, "If the killer thinks that he is killing, or the killed that he is killed, neither of them knows. That neither kills nor is it killed." The reality behind this is completely beyond space and time. Our whole notion of seeing a Universe within space and time is simply a mistake.

Beyond Space and Time

Dehabhimane galite vijnate paramatmani
Yatra, yatra manoyati, tatra, tatra samadhayah

"When body-consciousness has melted away,
and the Supreme Self has been realized,
Where, where the mind is sent, there, there it
gets Samadhi."

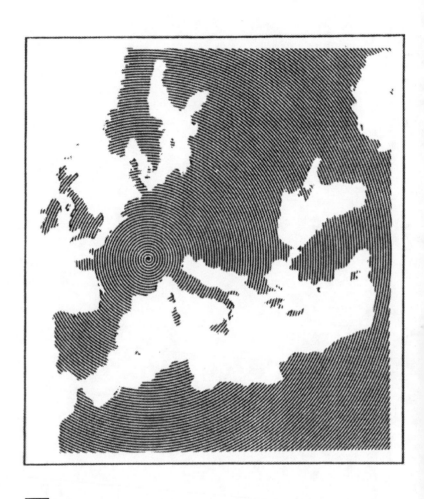

II Changes in the map of modern science

The Quest

Always the hope and expectation of science has been to find a beautiful simplicity underlying all the multifarious complexities of the visible world. We have traced the enormous variety in the life forms of this planet back through the long course of genetic evolution to very much simpler forms. The chemical energies on which most of these life forms function we have traced back to sunlight, and yet farther back to the gravitational energy of hydrogen dispersed in space. We have traced the materials of this sense world back to the ninety-two chemical elements which compose them, and, in the latter half of the present century, we have traced the ninety-two chemical elements, through stellar evolution, back to hydrogen. The farther back we trace it the simpler it looks, and always there lurks the hope that if we trace it back far enough we'll find that beautiful simplicity.

Beyond Space and Time

The same hope, of course, has driven the philosophers and the mystics, but, unlike the quest of many mystics and philosophers, the quest of those whom we call scientists has always been through the outside world, through questioning the external Universe – what is called the objective Universe. But how does the notion arise that the Universe exists outside and independent of the observer? How can we be sure that the external Universe is not conjured up by the observer himself?

The evidence that is usually pointed to is the agreement between the descriptions by various observers. If more than one observer can come to an agreement in the description of an event, it is usually presumed that the event could not have been conjured up by one of them. It is not that the descriptions need be identical, but only that the observers can reach an agreement on the nature of the event which, seen from their different points of view, would have given rise to their different descriptions. For example, two observers seeing an "object" in motion might disagree on the direction of its motion. One might see the object moving toward his right, while the other saw it moving toward the left. However, by understanding that one observer was facing north while the other faced south, they could immediately agree that what they saw was the same object. They understand that there is an objectivity in the series of events seen by both observers as the "moving object," and that the difference in their descriptions arose simply from the fact that they saw the "moving object" from different points of view.

A GEOMETRICAL PERSPECTIVE

The importance of our knowledge of geometry lies here. It is through a knowledge of geometry that we understand the objective identity of a series of events, even though the description of that series of events made by observers from different points of view may differ. It is through our knowledge of geometry - our knowledge of the space-time framework - that we understand the relationships between the points of view of the various observers.

Beyond Space and Time

Gradually, over the course of several centuries of scientific investigation, the notion has grown that objectivity is the final test of truth. The ultimate quest of science has gradually come to be the quest for the final objective reality which underlies the vast plethora of our varied observations and experiences. Partly this quest has taken the form of a deep investigation into the nature of matter and energy, and partly it has taken the form of a deep investigation into the nature of the space-time framework against which we understand the variety of points of view.

OBJECTIVITY

But curiously enough, it is just here, in the investigation of the space-time framework which supports the notion of objectivity, that we have run into trouble. It is not that the ultimate quest of our science is in trouble, but only the notion that objectivity is the final test of truth. As the subsequent sections of this paper will show, Einstein's relativity theory may be considered to be the last, brave attempt to save the notion that the objective observation by a plurality of observers is the final evidence for the reality of what is observed. We know now that that attempt has failed.

THE ILLUSION OF OBJECTIVITY

Now, in the last quarter of the twentieth century, through an understanding of the consequences of relativity theory, and through an understanding of apparitional causation, we can see, at last, that underneath the apparent complexities of gravity, electricity and inertia and under the apparent duality of perceiver and perceived there looms the utterly simple. This whole notion of objectivity was based on the assumption of plurality, on the assumption of separation between one observer and another and on the assumption of a separation between the perceiver and the perceived – a separation which can no longer be supported by our physics.

We were after a nice, simple, single statement of what exists, such that if we understood that single statement we could understand all this that we see. In a sense, the quest is done. The map is known. From our long investigation into the nature of the external, objective Universe we have finally found that that which exists behind all this is completely devoid of complexity.

In the introductory section of this book we have seen how the notion of apparitional causation forms the main feature in the cosmological map of Advaita Vedanta. This feature was totally absent from the cosmological map of classical physics which was based entirely on Newtonian mechanics and Euclidean geometry.

EINSTEIN

In this section we shall see how Einstein's insight has straightened out our understanding of geometry, and, subsequently, our understanding of matter and energy.

Then, at the end of this section, we shall see how these new understandings, by implication, point to an apparitional causation underlying the appearance of the primordial hydrogen.

The Quest

In the third section, entitled Joining the Maps, it will be pointed out how, following the introduction of the notion of apparitional causation to the map of modern science, we no longer have two maps, but only one. In this third section we shall examine some very interesting consequences which follow from the joining of the maps. In the fourth, and last, section we shall be concerned not so much with the map as with the possible journeys suggested by the map, and with the way our point of view has been colored by our long genetic past.

We start, now, with the first great change in the map of modern science. What we now understand as modern science followed this change.

Einstein's Equation of Separation

Swami Vivekananda, toward the end of the last century, tried to square Advaita Vedanta with what he referred to as "modern science." What we now refer to as modern science, or rather, modern physics, is something very different. What we, in this century, refer to as modern physics was not born until 1905, three years after Swamiji had passed away.

One of the most crucial measurements which pointed up the necessity for changing our point of view was made by Michelson and Morley in 1889, only three years after Sri Ramakrishna had passed away, but the explanation of the difficulty waited for Einstein in 1905.

MICHELSON AND MORLEY'S EXPERIMENT

Michelson and his friend Morley wanted to measure the speed of the earth through space – through what was then called the "luminiferous ether." Light was thought to be a wave motion and required a medium through which the waves might be conveyed. Sound waves travel through the air. Water

71

waves travel through the water. Likewise, it was thought, light waves travel through the "ether."

If canoes are moving through the waters of a still lake, it is simple to measure the motion of the canoes with respect to each other, but how do we measure the motion of the canoes with respect to the waters of the lake? We drop pebbles into the lake and measure the speed of the canoes with respect to the circles of ripples left on the surface of the water by the impact of the pebbles. "Likewise." Thought Michelson, "we'll drop a light wave into the ether and measure the motion of the earth with respect to the wave." It was an ingenious device, but the measurements always showed that the "waves" move along with the earth as if the earth were standing still with respect to the medium through which the waves were propagated. It is as though the circles of ripples left by our pebbles on the lake move along with our canoe. It is as though the occupants of all the canoes saw the circles of ripples moving along with their own canoes; not only the circles from the dropping of their

Einstein's Equation of Separation

own pebbles, but the circles left by the dropping of the other pebbles as well. Einstein said, "There is no lake! We have misunderstood the relation of space to time!"

EINSTEIN'S FOUR DIMENSIONAL UNIVERSE

Einstein pointed out that we live in a four-dimensional Universe, not a three-dimensional one. A three-dimensional Universe is not objective. If we are to see the Universe as objective, we must see it in four dimensions – we must put the equation of separation in four dimensions, that is, we must put time into the equation. We turn, then, for a closer look at the fascinating four-dimensional geometry of modern physics and its most unexpected consequence.

Changing Our Geometry

We start with a two-dimensional example. Pythagoras' theorem for two dimensions of space states that the square on the hypotenuse of a right triangle is equal to the sum of the squares on the sides forming the right angle.

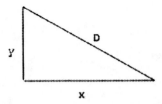

For a right triangle whose hypotenuse is D and whose sides are x and y, we write

$$D^2 = x^2 + y^2$$

Or, taking the square root of both sides,

$$D = \sqrt{x^2 + y^2}$$

This, then, is our equation of separation for two dimensions of space. The invention of this equation was not ascribed to Pythagoras until sometime after his death, and it is probable that he learned it during his visit to India, along with the pitch ratios of the strings of the Kithara.

Suppose two ships' captains wish to measure the distance between two islands which have an impassable reef between them. Suppose the first captain sails due north (by the stars) from one island until he sees the second island directly to his right (east). He has then simply to sail to his right until he reaches the island. Then, knowing the distance north that he sailed, and the distance east, by the use of Pythagoras' equation he can find the distance between the islands without having to cross the reef.

Suppose now that the second captain sails not due north by the stars, but sets his course by magnetic compass and sails magnetic north until he sees the other island directly to his right (not directly east). If, then, he sails directly to the island and knows the distances that his ship has moved, he, too, by the same equation, can calculate the distance between the islands. This distance is said to be

Changing Our Geometry

objective. Although the two captains chose different coordinate systems and differed in their estimates of how far north and east the second island was, they agree on the total distance between the islands. (However, it can easily be shown that this method of measurement and calculation does not give the objective distance between the islands. Pythagoras' equation is applicable only to a flat surface, a plane, but the surface of the Earth is curved. If the islands are several thousand miles apart, it becomes a three-dimensional problem.)

For a three-dimensional space the equation of separation between two points becomes

$$D = \sqrt{x^2 + y^2 + z^2}$$

where the directions x, y and z are taken perpendicular to each other.

Suppose we want to measure the distance diagonally across a room from the southeast corner at the floor to the northwest corner at the ceiling. If the walls and the floor are perpendicular to each other, we have simply to measure along the base of one wall to the far corner, then along the base of the far wall and, finally up the corner to the ceiling. These distances will be our x, our y and our z, and we have simply to square them, add them together, and take the square root of this sum to find the required distance.

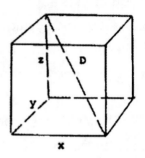

But the world is not objective in three dimensions either. We live in a Universe of four dimensions, and, as Einstein pointed out in 1905, time also must come into this equation if the equation is to remain invariant for observers moving with respect to each other. Our problem is not how to measure from the southeast corner at the floor to the northwest corner at the ceiling but, rather, how to measure the total separation, the four-dimensional separation, between an event at one of those corners and another event at the other.

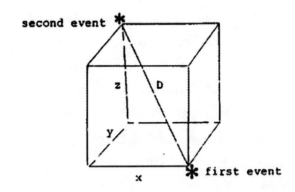

Our difficulty arises because the distance alone turns out not to be objective. That is, two people moving with respect to each other measure different distances between those events. Also, the time separation between two such events is not objective. Observers moving with respect to each other disagree on the length of time that has elapsed between two events. Only four-dimensional addresses such as here-now or there-then are objective, and

Beyond Space and Time

the separation between any two such addresses (events) is also objective.

Here, "moving with respect to each other" corresponds to our two ships' captains choosing different coordinate systems, i.e., choosing different directions along which to measure north or east. Just as our ships' captains differed in their estimates of the distances north and east to the second island, just so, two observers moving with respect to each other might differ in their estimates of the space and time separations between two events. But just as our ships' captains agreed on the total distance between the islands, just so, our two observers, moving with respect to each other, will agree on the total separation between any two events.

Einstein's equation of separation takes the form

$$S = \sqrt{x^2 + y^2 + z^2 - t^2}$$

We write S instead of D because the four-dimensional separation is no longer simply a

Changing Our Geometry

distance between here and there, but rather, a space-time separation between here-now and there-then.

Now S is invariant, that is, if we agree to measure the distances x, y and z in the same units and the time, t, in a corresponding unit, then the separation, S, between any two events will be seen to be the same to all observers regardless of their states of motion with respect to each other. S is invariant, i.e., it is objective. It is the same for all observers regardless of their motion or their points of view.

(Einstein never liked the term relativity theory. He wanted it called the theory of invariants.)

This, then, is our new geometry designed to save the objectivity of the Universe. But does it? For any two events, say here-now and there-then, this equation can be simplified to

$$S = \sqrt{x^2 - t^2}$$

Beyond Space and Time

So long as the x direction is chosen from here to there or from there to here, so that y and z are zero.

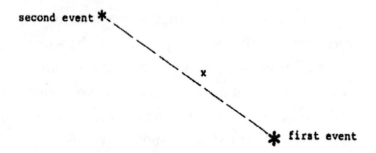

It should be noted that time comes into this equation as minus t^2, so that if one observer sees a greater distance, x, between two events, he will also see a greater time, t. Between the events here-now and there-then, one observer will see a greater distance between here and there and a greater time between now and then. It is only the total separation, S, that is objective, or invariant.

A WRONG UNDERSTANDING
OF SPACE AND TIME

Suppose that, standing here on earth, we see two space ships approaching, one from the right and one from the left, in opposite directions. Let us suppose that, as seen by us, each of them will pass our position at 99% of the speed of light, one from right to left and one from left to right so that they pass very close to each other. Seen from our ordinary understanding of space and time, we would say that the space ships will pass, that is the passengers in each ship will see the other ship passing by, at 99 + 99 or 198% of the speed of light. But that is wrong. Our ordinary understanding of space and time is wrong. We know from our measurements of physics that particles never interact as if they were passing at speeds greater than or equal to the speed of light. We know from our measurements of high-speed particles that the passengers of each space ship would see the other ship passing by at 99.995% of the speed of light. Each of us will see the other's time measurements as "wrong" and the other's space measurements, in the direction of the motion, as "wrong." But we will all agree on the total separation between any two events both of which can be seen from all three positions. With the help of our new geometry, our four-dimensional geometry, we can understand the relationship of our several points of view so that we can still see both events as objective and the separation between the two events as also objective.

SPACE AND TIME AS OPPOSITES

With the equation of separation in this form, $S = \sqrt{x^2 - t^2}$, *it becomes immediately obvious that space and time are opposites because where x and t are equal, S = 0.* That is, for the events here-now and there-then, if the space separation between here and there is equal to the time separation between now and then, then the total separation between here-now and there-then is zero. This is true for all observers regardless of the orientation of their coordinate systems in space, and regardless of their motion with respect to each other. It is objectively zero.

NO

Under what conditions is it true that the total separation will be zero? Is it simply a trivial case? No, it is by no means trivial, because it is true for any two events one of

84

which can be seen from the other. If what we call a light beam can go from the event there-then to the event here-now, or from here-now to there-then, then the events must be considered adjacent, that is, the total separation between them must be zero. It is true for every event of our perception. The separation between the event of perception and the event perceived is zero. We see the whole Universe in the past. We cannot see anything when it happens. We can't see the back of our hands now. We see everything late. Every event that we see as away from us in space we see backwards in time, and it is only on the basis of such perceptions, where the separation between the perceiver and the perceived is zero, that we have come to the conclusion in the first place that the Universe exists outside.

The ancients used to say that "the mind goes out through the eye and takes the form of a pot." The moderns say that "the photons come in from the pot and take a form in the eye." The equation says that it makes no difference which mistake we make -- the separation is zero. In an effort to save the objectivity of the Universe, we have had to abandon the separation between the perceiver and the perceived.

THERE-THEN

The Universe which we see is set up in this very peculiar way so that we cannot see anything when it happens. We see the whole show in the past. If we see an event in the Andromeda Galaxy at a distance of two and a quarter million light years from us, we see it two and a quarter million years ago. Why? Usually we say that it is because light travels at a finite velocity. But really, of course, it is because *what we call the speed of light is simply the ratio of space to time.* One light year is equal to one year. And we see a Universe as if outside of us by this elaborate trick of seeing everything as back in time, and in just such a way that the total separation between the perceiver and the perceived remains zero.

THE SEPARATION BETWEEN THE PERCEIVER AND THE PERCEIVED IS ZERO

It is not clear that any Advaita Vedantin, in ancient time, understood clearly that space and time are opposites, but it is clear that they understood that the separation between the perceiver and the perceived is zero. As Shankara says in the first three verses of the Dakshinamurti Stotram:

Seeing the Universe existing within himself, like a city seen in a mirror, yet appearing as if produced outside, through Maya or apparition, as in sleep...

He who, through his own will, like a mighty magician or some great yogi, spreads out this Universe which exists indeterminate, like the germ of a seed, and is later on diversified by the difference arising from the notion of space and time created by Maya...

He whose existence is the substance of such fictitious notions as I am the body or I am the doer, who is the direct illumination of those who realize the identity of the perceiver and the perceived, and through the immediate perception of whom there is no more return to the ocean of worldly existence, to him, incarnate as the teacher, to him be this salutation!

Einstein's Equation Of Mass and Energy

In the previous discussion we noted the grave change introduced by relativity theory in our understanding of the space-time framework within which we seem to see a Universe of objective events involving changes in matter and energy – involving changes in the states of rest or motion of material bodies and transformations in their energies. But the change introduced by relativity theory in our understanding of that mass and that energy is equally grave and, as we shall see in the subsequent discussions, it has taken us far in our search for the utterly simple which constitutes the goal of the scientific quest and which underlies the apparent complexity of this Universe of gravity, electricity and inertia. This is the second great change that was required in our physics to make possible the joining of the cosmological map of European science with that of Advaita Vedanta.

OPPOSITES

The physics of the last century took for granted that the Universe was objective in three dimensions and that it consisted of real particles with real mass and real energy moving through real space in real time. Mass was considered to be one thing and energy, another. Space was considered to be one thing and time, another. It had not yet been noticed that space and time are opposites and that they must, therefore, in some sense, be identical. By opposites, in physics, we mean two quantities, like a plus and minus electrical charges, which are related in such a way that, in some sense, if we have the same amount of both it is like having none of either. If in an atom the positive charges on the nucleus are balanced by the negative charges of the electron cloud around it, the total charge on that atom is zero.

We also understand that in order for two things to be opposite they must, in some sense, be identical. Plus and minus electrical charges are opposites only by being identical in that they are both electrical charges. It's like money into the bank and money out of the bank.

Einstein's Equation Of Mass and Energy

Rupees into the bank and Rupees out of the bank are opposites because they are both Rupees. Dollars into the bank and dollars out of the bank are opposites because they are both dollars. There is no such thing as the opposite of a dog. Space and time are opposites in the sense that if, between two events, the space separation is equal to the time separation then the total separation between those two events is zero. Between the event of perception and the event perceived the space separation exists only by contrast to the time separation, and the time separation exists only by contrast to the space separation. They are identical in that together they form the two halves of the framework within which we seem to see a Universe of mass and energy. We turn now to a discussion of that mass and that energy.

A 19TH CENTURY DEFINITION OF MASS

Long before the end of the last century we had understood that the inertia, or mass, of a physical body was measured by the resistance which that body offered to changes in its state of rest or motion. Newton, in 1666, put it quite beautifully:

Corpus omne perseverare in statu suo quiescendi vel movendi uniformiter in directum, nisi quatenus illud a viribus impressis cogitur statum suum mutare.

(Bodies all persevere in their states of quiescence or of motion, uniform in direction, unless, by forces impressed upon them, they are compelled to change their states.)

GRAVITY, ELECTRICITY AND INERTIA

Now it is quite singular that matter should behave in this way - that it should resist changes in its states of rest or motion - and this behavior, like the existence of the electrical and gravitational fields, cannot be explained by classical physics. Gravity, electricity, inertia and the conservation laws which govern transformational causation are completely inexplicable by that causation. They are completely inexplicable to classical physics.

But matter does behave in this way. If, in a moving vehicle, you collide with another vehicle, which has pulled to a stop on the

Einstein's Equation Of Mass and Energy

highway in front of you, the consequences to your vehicle depend largely on the mass of the other vehicle. The greater its mass, the greater the resistance which it will offer to changes in its motion on impact. Often we measure the mass of an object by the resistance which it offers to being shaken. A man in a blindfold can easily distinguish a baseball from a tennis ball simply by shaking it. It requires energy to throw a baseball only because the mass of the ball offers resistance to every change in its state of rest or motion. Likewise, energy is required to catch it or to change the direction of its motion with a baseball bat.

Mostly we study physics in the playground, and we understand it in our muscles. But here on earth, where the gravitational field is about the same from playground to playground, we sometimes think that the mass of an object may be measured by the resistance which that object offers to being picked up. But that is wrong – or, rather, only partly true. Weight, or the resistance of an object to being picked up, varies with the strength of the gravitational field against which it is being picked up. On the Moon, where the gravitational field is much less than in our playgrounds on Earth, a baseball would offer much less resistance to being picked up. On the Moon it would weigh only one-sixth as much as it weighs on Earth, but it would be just as hard to shake – every bit as hard.

ENERGY IN CLASSICAL PHYSICS

Energy, in classical physics, was understood as the capacity to do work – the capacity to effect changes in the states of rest or motion of matter. A force is measured by the *rate* of change which it produces in the state of motion of a given mass. *Energy* is measured by the *total_change*. When we wind up a clock, we wind it up against the force of the spring, but it is *how far* we wind against that force which determines the energy of the wound spring and, therefore, how long the clock will run. When we pick up a weight from the floor, we pick it up against the force of gravity, but it is how far we pick it up against that force which determines the energy of the raised weight and what it might do on falling. The energy of the raised weight is determined by the product of the weight (the force exerted by gravity at that particular place on that mass) and the distance through which work has been done against that weight (against that force).

CONSERVATION OF ENERGY

Now energy, like mass, is a conserved quantity. What is meant by that is that in any transformation of energy, the total amount of energy which we have at the end is exactly the same as the total amount which we had at the beginning, even though the form of that energy may have changed. If a baseball is thrown straight up with a certain kinetic energy, it will reach a certain height where its kinetic energy will have disappeared completely. Working against gravity on the way up, the kinetic energy has been transformed to gravitational energy which, on the way down, is re-transformed to kinetic energy so that (overlooking friction) the ball will reach the ground with the same amount of kinetic energy which it had when it began its rise. We all understand this in our muscles, and it is important to remember that we do.

ENERGY AND INERTIA

The energy of a physical system was defined as the capacity of that system to *produce* changes in the state of rest or motion of a body of a given mass. The *inertia*, or mass, of a physical body was defined as the capacity of that body to *resist* changes in its state of rest or motion. Energy is the capacity to produce such changes, and mass is the capacity to resist them. In this sense mass and energy were understood, in classical physics, to be opposites. What we had not noticed is that in order to be opposites they must, in some sense be identical. Their identity became obvious from Einstein's equations.

EINSTEIN'S EQUATIONS

Einstein's equations led to a revolution in our physics. Our entire system of physics was wrong and required to be corrected for this new understanding. We had misunderstood the relationship of space and time and with it the relationship of mass and energy. From the

Einstein's Equation Of Mass and Energy

equations of relativity it followed that, for a particle at rest, its energy *is* its mass. It was like a mountain having two names because it had been seen from two different points of view without the realization that both views were of the same mountain. That which we had been measuring all along as mass turned out to be some kind of energy, and, for a particle at rest, Einstein's equation of mass and energy states that

$$E = m.$$

This equation is often written as $E = mc^2$, but the c^2 is necessary only if we refuse to measure space and time in commensurate units. If space is to be measured in centimeters then time should be measured in "jiffies." A jiffy is the length of time required for light to travel one centimeter. The speed of light, c, is then one centimeter per jiffy and c^2 goes to unity, and we have Einstein's original equation, $E = m$.

The energy of a particle varies with its motion but the energy which a particle has when not in motion, that is, the energy which a particle *is* when seen at rest is called its rest energy or its rest mass. But what kind of energy is it?

WHAT IS HYDROGEN?

As mentioned earlier, all the matter of the observable Universe can be traced back to hydrogen, dispersed through space and falling together by gravity to galaxies and stars. The other chemical elements are fashioned from hydrogen at extreme temperatures in the bellies of stars and in the brilliant stellar explosions which scatter those heavy elements through interstellar space. The problem is to understand the hydrogen, because the mass of these other elements is just the mass of the original hydrogen out of which these other elements have been built. Here, at last, through relativity theory, we are able to understand that the mass of that hydrogen is simply some kind of energy. But what kind of energy? It is a tremendous simplification to understand that, for particles at rest, their mass is their energy. But what kind of energy is the

Einstein's Equation Of Mass and Energy

mass of the primordial hydrogen from which the entire Universe arises by transformation?

Suppose we have two identical clocks. One we wind up; the other we leave unwound. Which one is more massive? Which one will be harder to shake? The wound one will be harder to shake because it is wound up against the resistance of the spring and will therefore have a greater energy and a greater mass. Now against what are the protons and the electrons of the primordial hydrogen wound up to give them their mass?

THE REST MASS OF HYDROGEN

The problem is simplified by the fact that we have only a few kinds of energy from which to choose – gravity, kinetic energy, radiation, electricity, magnetism and nuclear energy. It is further simplified by the fact that kinetic energy, radiation and magnetism cannot exist at rest and cannot, therefore, give rise to the rest energy of the primordial hydrogen. We are left, then, to choose between gravity, electricity and nuclear energy. Since we are living in what is called the nuclear age of physics, many would think that the choice should go to nuclear energy, but that might be wrong. Even if the matter of the Universe began as hydrogen, which has the maximum *available* nuclear energy, and ended as iron, which has the least, even then the nuclear energy released to other forms could account for only about one percent of the rest mass of that matter. Therefore, the choice must go to gravity, electricity, or both.

DIFFERENT GRAVITATIONAL WIND-UPS

Embodied beings such as ourselves have a genetic response to being wound up against gravity. We have a fear of heights. We have muscles to handle the problem if we jump down from a chair because the wind-up of climbing to the seat of a chair is not very great. But very few of us have muscles capable of handling the problem if we jump down from the edge of the roof, because the gravitational energy represented by our bodies on the roof is more than our muscles can handle on landing. None of us has muscles to handle the problem if we fall from an airplane or from a high cliff

Einstein's Equation Of Mass and Energy

because the gravitational energy represented by the physical separation of our bodies from the ground is simply too great. The farther away from the earth our bodies are, the more wound up they are and, therefore, the more massive they are.

However, the gravitational wind-up in picking our bodies up from the surface of the earth represents only a minute fraction of their total gravitational wind-up because the surface of the earth in no way represents the gravitational floor of the Universe. An object falling to the surface of the earth, even from outer space, comes in with a kinetic energy only a few times greater than the energy needed to vaporize that object.

An object falling to the surface of the Sun would develop considerably more kinetic energy because the gravitational field at the surface of the Sun is nearly thirty times as strong as the gravitational field at the surface of the earth. The surface of the Sun represents a lower floor, and the farther down we fall, the more gravitational energy is converted to kinetic energy, and, therefore, the more dangerous it is when we land.

But there are collapsed stars, such as black dwarf stars, with a density of a hundred thousand pounds per pint where the consequences of falling would be quite severe. And there are neutron stars, collapsed to a density of perhaps a hundred thousand battleships per pint, where falling would develop kinetic energies equivalent to about ten percent of the rest mass of the falling objects. The splash of a ten-gram marshmallow falling to the surface of such a star would have enough energy to evaporate a town. It would have the energy of one atom bomb. But the total energy of a ten-gram marshmallow is equal to the energy of ten atom bombs. Is there a still lower floor to the Universe to which we might drop the marshmallow to convert its *entire* rest energy to kinetic energy? Yes, theoretically there is. If all the matter of the observable Universe were in one place, that would be the floor.

Einstein's Equation Of Mass and Energy

THE GRAVITATIONAL
WIND-UP OF THE UNIVERSE

The mass of the Universe, as we see it now, is equal to the energy required to pick it up, or space it out, from that floor. The Universe is wound up against gravity – it is massive – just by being dispersed. We can understand the mass of the protons as due to the fact that they are not all in one place. It is that simple.

The curious thing is that we can understand the rest mass of the hydrogen from an entirely different consideration. The hydrogen atom is made of electrical particles – one proton and one electron – and they have opposite charges. Now since opposite charges attract each other, there should be a certain amount of energy represented by the fact that the charges are separated from each other. That, however, would be only a small part of the energy. A great deal more energy is represented by the smallness of the particles themselves. Like charges repel each other.

ELECTRICAL WIND-UP

We may put this another way: Like charge repels itself. We can see, then, that the smaller the geometrical size of a given charge, the greater the electrical energy represented by its smallness because its smallness represents pushing like charge toward itself. If a single, electrical charge were allowed to become infinitely big, its rest mass would go to zero. If a single, electrical charge were forced to become infinitely small, its rest mass would go to infinity. It is only because this charge is seen squeezed down against itself to a finite size that it has a finite rest mass. Seen from this point of view, we can understand the rest energy of the primordial hydrogen as due entirely to the smallness of the electrical charges.

Thus, we have two apparently different and seemingly independent ways of accounting for the rest energy of the primordial hydrogen. It is wound up against its gravitational field because the atoms are seen spaced out, and it is wound up against its electrical field because the atoms are seen to be composed of minute electrical particles. (And it is wound up against Heisenberg's uncertainty principle because we see it in space and time.)

Einstein's Equation Of Mass and Energy

But *spacing out* against the gravitational field and *spacing in* against the electrical field are themselves opposites. The primordial hydrogen is massive because it is seen as spaced out against the condensational gravitational field and spaced in against the dispersional electrical field. Between two protons, gravity pulls and electricity pushes. In this sense, they are clearly opposites.

Yet both operate on the inverse square law. Between two objects, the gravitational field, like the electrical field, falls off inversely as the square of the distance between them. If the distance is doubled, the pull or push falls off to one-quarter. If the distance is increased threefold, it falls off to one-ninth. The remarkable thing is that no other fields fall off in this way, and that the strengths of the fields are such that the rest energy of the primordial hydrogen turns out to be the same when looked at from either side.

REST ENERGY

Rest energy is simply a geometrical wind-up. Both the gravitational and the electrical

105

rest energies of the primordial hydrogen are what are called energies of position in space. Although one is wound up against space by dispersion and one by condensation, they are both wound up against space, and without space they are inconceivable. They are opposite in the direction of wind-up, but identical in that they are both wound up against space on the inverse square law. (It might be helpful to our understanding if we simply dropped the words 'gravity' and 'electricity' and thought of the one as the result of dispersion and the other as the result of smallness or condensation.)

When we break a cookie, we require space in which to break it. There must be space between the parts. Likewise, if we break it to crumbs, there must be space around the crumbs. Further, the more divided it is, the smaller the parts. To say that it is divided is to say that it is small. You can't break a cookie into larger and larger parts. Dividedness and smallness are but one idea. In this sense, *electricity and gravity are identical.*

Einstein's Equation Of Mass and Energy

$$E = m$$

In the previous paragraphs no mention has been made of time. But space cannot exist except by contrast to time. We live in a four-dimensional Universe. We see momentum in the x direction, momentum in the y direction, momentum in the z direction and momentum in the time direction. The time component of the momentum is the energy. It is only through relativity theory, through an understanding that space and time are identical as well as opposite, and that neither can exist without the other, that we have come, at last, to understand that energy and mass are also identical as well as opposite and that neither can exist without the other. For a particle at rest, its energy *is* its mass. E = m. It is energy itself which is hard to shake.

Apparitional Causation

The first great change in the map of modern science, and on which is based what we now call modern physics, was Einstein's discovery that space and time are seen as a pair of opposites on an underlying identity. (It is not that he saw things in quite this way, but rather that this way of seeing things follows directly from his equations.) The second great change was in our ideas of mass and energy, and the third was in our ideas of causation. Classical physics, the physics of Swamiji's day, like Sankhya, believed only in transformational causation. It was materialistic and mechanistic and took for granted the separation between the perceiver and the perceived.

We know now that the physics of Swamiji's day was wrong. We know now that the Universe cannot arise by transformational causation. It is observational rather than actual and must arise by apparition. We see now that the discrimination between mass and energy has melted away. The discrimination between space and time has melted away. And we shall presently see that even the discrimination between mass-energy and space-time has melted away. We can see now what Swamiji must have seen then, that Advaita Vedanta could never be squared with classical physics. The physics wasn't ready. He, himself, tried to straighten it out by assigning to Nikola Tesla the task of showing, mathematically, that mass and energy (Akasha and Prana) are one. (*Complete Works*, vol. 5, Fifth Edition, 1947, p.77). At that time, Albert Einstein was just a boy. Had Tesla succeeded in this effort, the history of modern physics might have been very different indeed.

We have noted the fundamental changes introduced by relativity theory in our understanding of the interrelationships of mass, energy, space and time. Now we must study the changes which those changes have wrought in our model of the "objective reality" which, it was thought, must underlie the Universe of our physics. We must see, now, where our quest has led.

Our quest was for an utter simplicity underlying the world of our perceptions, and the quest took the form of a pursuit of what we thought was the objective reality. It was this pursuit of objectivity that led to the breakdown of our notion of the separateness of space and time and, through that, to the breakdown of our notion of the separateness of mass and energy.

As mentioned earlier, in the last century we believed that the Universe consisted of real particles with real mass and real energy moving through real space in real time. Mass, energy, space and time were all considered to be independent entities. This point of view may conveniently be represented by a diagram where the lines of the diagram represent the old lines of demarcation between mass, energy, space and time.

mass	space
energy	time

Beyond Time and Space

THE WORLD OF CLASSICAL PHYSICS

Since 1905, however, we have come to understand that the horizontal line drops out of the diagram because space and time are not independent of each other, nor are mass and energy. But we now see that the vertical line must also drop out of the diagram because the mass-energy discontinuum on the left is simply a geometrical wind-up against the space-time continuum on the right. The electrical and gravitational fields are features of the space-time framework against which the particles are wound up. Yet without the particles there would be no fields. Each structures the other. Without the fields there would be no particles, and without the particles there would be no fields.

It must be borne in the mind that we are here talking physics. We are not talking philosophy. It might be conceivable, from the standpoint of our genetic understanding of space and time, to think of space as an empty nothingness existing in the absence of matter. But space is not an empty nothingness. It is characterized by the electrical and gravitational fields which themselves determine both the structure and the behavior of the material particles. Just as mass and energy structure space and time, so also space and time structure mass and energy.

Now when these lines of demarcation between mass, energy, space and time are obliterated, all our lines of demarcation are gone, for without the notion of mass, length or time it is impossible to define any quantity referred to in our physics, and we are left not with a model of a Universe, but only with a question mark.

?

What is the reality behind the world of classical physics?

Here it becomes impossible to make any positive statement about the reality which underlies our physics, but our inquiry is not yet closed because we can still ask some roundabout questions and get answers in terms of negation. We can still ask, "What could not exist in the absence of space or in the absence of time?" These questions can be answered. We have already seen that dividedness and smallness can exist only in space and that change can exist only in time. What exists beyond space and time must, therefore, be chang*eless*, *in*finite and *un*divided.

$$? \quad = \quad \begin{array}{l} \text{changeless} \\ \text{infinite} \\ \text{undivided} \end{array}$$

It should be noted that these are purely negative statements, but that they must apply to whatever exists behind the appearance of the primordial hydrogen which is, itself, divided, finite and changing. Hydrogen is very finely divided. It is divided into atoms. It is grossly finite. It is composed of minute electrical particles. And it is continually changing. It falls together into galaxies and stars. Our problem is, "How, if the reality is changeless, infinite and undivided, do we come to see the changing, the finite and the divided?" First, it is perfectly clear that our present perception of a changing, finite and divided Universe could not have come about by transformational causation. The changeless could not have been changed into the changing, since that would require change in the changeless. Also, hydrogen is made out of energy and energy cannot arise by a transformation of energy. That would be like making milk out of milk. Milk is not made out of milk. It is made out of a mixture of cows and grass. Just as gold cannot be made by remolding gold, just so energy cannot arise by transformations of energy. The only kind of causation, if it can be called causation at all, that could give rise to energy – that could give rise to change in the changeless – is a causation by apparition. It is the kind of thing that happens when you mistake a rope for a snake, or when you mistake your friend for a ghost.

Now when you mistake your friend for a ghost, three things are necessary. First, you must fail to see your friend rightly, or there would be no mistake. Second, the ghost must be different from your friend. Otherwise, again, no mistake would be made. And third, in order to mistake your friend for a ghost *you had to see your friend*. It is your friend whom you have mistaken for a ghost, and the characteristics of your friend will show up in the ghost. If your friend is tall and thin, the ghost will be tall and thin, and if your friend is roly-poly, you'll see a roly-poly ghost.

If, then, we have seen the changeless, the infinite, the undivided as something *else*, that else must be changing, finite and divided because in this case *there is no other else*.

It was pointed out long ago by Shankara that in order to mistake a rope for a snake we require the mental impression left from the previous experience of a snake. It is only on the basis of such an impression that we conjure up the illusory snake rather than an illusory stick or an illusory crack in the ground. Whatever we conjure up we conjure up on the basis of some previous experience. Likewise, he suggested, when we mistake the changeless, the infinite, the undivided for the changing, the finite, the divided, we require the previous

Apparitional Causation

experience of the latter. In this case, however, we need not fall back on the necessity of previous experience. Seeing the changeless as anything else means seeing it as changing. Likewise, seeing the infinite and the undivided as anything else means seeing it as finite and divided since in this case there is no other else. There is one further difficulty with his suggestion. Time is part of this else. To what, then could "previous" refer?

Now in order to see the undivided as divided, we had to see the undivided. In order to see your friend as a ghost, you had to see your friend. And just as the characteristics of your friend must show up in the ghost for which she is mistaken, just so the undividedness must show up in the divided for which it is mistaken, and that is what we see as gravity. If you see the reality as divided and dispersed, it will show the tendency to all come back together like a stretched rubber band. Likewise, in order to see the infinite as finite, we had to see the infinite, and that infinite, seen in the apparently finite, is what we see as electricity. If you see the reality as minute particles, those particles will necessarily be electrical (i.e., the electrical energy of an electrical particle goes to zero only if the size of that particle goes to infinity). And, finally, in order to see the changeless as changing, you had to see the changeless, and that changeless, seen in the apparently changing, is what we see as inertia. If you see the reality as moving, it will show a tendency to coast.

Space is not that which separates the many, but that which seems to separate the one, and in that space that oneness shines, therefore falls whatever falls. Again, space is not that in which we see the small, but that in which the infinite appears as small, and in that space that vastness shines, therefore bursts whatever bursts, therefore shines whatever shines. And finally, time is not that in which we see the changing, but that in which the changeless seems to change, and in that time that changeless shines, therefore rests whatever rests, therefore coasts whatever coasts.

It is hopeless to try to understand this Universe without understanding apparitional

Apparitional Causation

causation. Swamiji, of course, knew that. The only reason that Swamiji failed to square Advaita with physics was because the physics of his day could not be squared with fact. The theory could not be squared with the observations. It was only after the introduction of apparitional causation, through relativity theory, that it became possible to square our physics with the observations, and with Advaita Vedanta.

Swamiji said in London (*Complete Works*, Vol. 2, Seventh Edition, 1948, p. 130) that, "This absolute has become the Universe by coming through time, space and causation. This is the central idea of Advaita. Time, space and causation are like the glass through which the absolute is seen, and when it is seen on the lower side it appears as the Universe."

It is here, in apparitional causation, that we understand, for the first time, the physics behind gravity, electricity and inertia. It is apparitional physics – what we shall here call "square one physics."

It is here, in apparitional causation, that we understand the physics behind those old

Beyond Time and Space

Sanskrit terms Asti, Bhati and Priya. Here, too, it is apparitional physics. Every object of our perception is said to be characterized by existence, Asti, perceptibility, Bhati, and dearness, Priya. Asti is the changeless, seen in the apparently changing. Bhati is the infinite seen in the apparently finite. And Priya is the undivided seen in the apparently divided. Whatever transformations we see here are ultimately driven from square one. Mass and energy, space and time, gravity, electricity, inertia and the conservation laws arise in square one. The intergalactic hydrogen arises in square one.

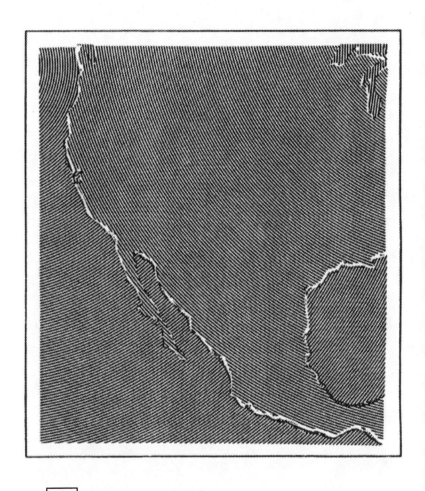

| III | Joining the maps

Introduction

Swami Vivekananda, early in the year 1896, wrote in a letter to an English friend, "Mr. Tesla thinks he can demonstrate mathematically that force and matter are reducible to potential energy. I am to go and see him next week to get this new mathematical demonstration. In that case the Vedantic cosmology will be placed on the surest of foundations. I am working a good deal now upon the cosmology and eschatology of the Vedanta. I clearly see their perfect union with modern science, and the elucidation of the one will be followed by that of the other."

(*Complete Works*, Vol. 5, Fifth Edition, 1947, p. 77).

Here Swamiji uses the terms force and matter for the Sanskrit terms Prana and Akasha. Tesla used the Sanskrit terms and apparently understood them as energy and mass. (In Swamiji's day, as in many dictionaries published in the first half of the present century, force and energy were not always clearly differentiated. Energy is a more proper translation of the Sanskrit term Prana.)

Beyond Time and Space

Tesla apparently failed in his effort to show the identity of mass and energy. Apparently he understood that when speed increases, mass must decrease. He seems to have thought that mass might be "converted" to energy and vice versa, rather than that they were identical in some way, as is pointed out in Einstein's equations. At any rate, Swamiji seems to have sensed where the difficulty lay in joining the maps of European science and Advaita Vedanta and set Tesla to solve the problem. It is apparently in the hope that Tesla would succeed in this that Swamiji says, "In that case the Vedantic cosmology will be placed on the surest of foundations." Unfortunately Tesla failed and the solution did not come till nine years later, in a paper by Albert Einstein. But by then Swamiji was gone, and the connection of the maps was delayed.

One, Two, Three and Many

The Advaita Vedantins are Vivartavadins, that is, they understand that the "first cause" is apparitional. And in that domain their map is quite adequate. But in the domain of transformational causation, which follows from the first cause, their map is somewhat sketchy. The map of European science, on the other hand, is quite thorough in the domain of transformational causation but simply points, through Einstein's equations, to the underlying apparition.

FROM APPARITION TO TRANSFORMATION

What we call "square one physics" arises by apparition. What we call the physics of square two to square twelve arises by transformation. The problem of joining the maps is the problem of joining square one and square two. The problem is how, from the nature of the reality, which the Advaita Vedantins call Brahman (or Atman), do we come, through apparitional causation, which the Advaita Vedantins call Maya, to the world of transformational causation – to the

125

perception of the primordial hydrogen, a gas made up of positive and negative electrical particles (the protons and the electrons), widely dispersed through space and falling together by gravity to galaxies and stars. Why do we see hydrogen and not something else?

Swami Ashokananda once said, "Give me two and I'll give you a million." The problem is how to get two. That is the problem of the first cause, and we have seen that it is apparitional and that through it we already get three and many.

PANCHAMAHABHUTA SUTRAS

But let us go through it step by step, starting with a quote of the first lines of the *Panchamahabhuta Sutras*, a little-known text on Advaita Vedanta, which itself begins with a quote from Chandogya Upanishad.

1. "All this is Brahman. Let a man meditate on that visible world as beginning, ending and breathing in it, the Brahman."

2. Now mind is, as it were, a sense of otherness in That.

One, Two, Three and Many

3. In the changeless. In the infinite. In the undivided.

4. Its appearance is through the Gunas of which ignorance, Maya is made.

5. Concealing, projecting, yet revealing, in the projected, something of that which is concealed.

6. As something of the rope is revealed in the snake for which it is mistaken.

7. As if, being hidden, through the veiling power of Tamas, the nature of Brahman, through the revealing power of Sattva, shone in the otherness for which, through the projecting power of Rajas, it is, as it were, mistaken.

8. By this Vivarta, the changeless, the infinite, the undivided as Asti-Bhati-Priya.

9. Giving rise to Parinama (transformation) in the causal, the subtle and the gross.

PHYSICAL AND MENTAL

The thrust of the eighth and ninth sutras is that it is the nature of the reality, seen through the revealing power of Sattva as Asti-Bhati-

Beyond Time and Space

Priya that drives whatever is driven in the phenomenal Universe, whether physical or mental. We have seen that in the physical Universe the changeless shows as inertia, the infinite as electricity and the undivided as gravity. But in the mental world also we feel driven. We feel driven toward peace and love and freedom. The search for the changeless shows as the yearning for peace, the search for the undivided shows as love, and the search for the infinite shows as the yearning for freedom. It is not that our bodies don't fall in search of the undivided. They do. It's just that our brains are genetically programmed to re-direct the search in ways which lead, through action, through transformational causation, to the perpetuation of the race.

To living beings like ourselves, love appears quite different from gravity. The yearning for freedom and the self-repulsion of like electrical charges appear quite different. And the yearning for peace appears as quite different from inertia – the tendency of matter to continue in a given state of motion. But as seen from the standpoint of the apparitional mechanism by which these pairs arise, they do not seem very different at all. They are simply the effect of what, in Sanskrit, is called Asti-Bhati-Priya. They are simply the nature of the reality seen through space and time, and it is only the situations in which they arise that make love and gravity seem so different. Love arises between living beings who see themselves as perceivers. Gravity arises between material particles which are seen by the living organisms as the perceived. The yearning for peace and love and freedom is related to the genetic programming, whereas the existence of gravity, electricity and inertia is seen even in the perceived.

These two apparently different manifestations of Asti-Bhati-Priya are said, in Sanskrit, to function in different spaces. The yearning for peace and love and freedom is said to be in the mind-space while gravity, electricity and inertia are said to function in the great-space (physical space).

Beyond Time and Space

The Advaita Vedantins speak of three states of consciousness, the causal, the subtle and the gross. Each is said to be associated with its own space. The causal state is associated with what is called the consciousness space, Chidakasha. In that space there is said to be no consciousness of plurality, but only the consciousness of the duality of "I" and "Thou," the perceiver and the perceived. There, Asti-Bhati-Priya is represented as Shiva-Shakti. The prostrate figure of Shiva represents the supreme peace of the changeless. The female figure of Shakti (energy), dancing on his chest, represents the undivided and the infinite. Her blissful aspect represents the undivided, while her terrible aspect represents the infinite. If it be asked why the infinite is represented by terror rather than by freedom, the answer is that Shiva-Shakti represents the perceived rather than the perceiver. Infinitude in the perceiver is freedom. In the perceived it is terror.

One, Two, Three and Many

THE SUBTLE AND THE GROSS SPACE

In each of the other spaces there is said to be the consciousness of plurality as well as duality. In the subtle state there is consciousness of a plurality in the perceiver, the consciousness of a plurality of minds (egos) in the mind space (Chittakasha). And in the gross state, which corresponds to the perception of the physical Universe, there is the perception of a plurality of things in the great space (Mahakasha), the space which seems to separate the stars.

WHY THREE SPACES?

Given the nature of the reality and the nature of the apparition as described by the Advaita Vedantins, it is easy to see how these three spaces arise. If what exists is one and you see it as two, then you, the perceiver, must be one of those two. (Otherwise there are three already.) This is the duality of the perceiver and the perceived, and their separation, like any apparent separation, must be seen in a space. Space is that which seems to separate two or many.

Given this duality, if a plurality is seen, it must be seen on this duality. The plurality may be seen either in the perceiver or in the perceived. The former gives rise to the perception of a plurality of minds (egos) in the mind-space, and the latter, to the perception of a plurality of protons in the great-space. If it be asked why protons rather than electrons or something else, the answer is that it is the proton, not the electrons or something else, which has its rest mass related to the gravitational plurality as well as to the electrical duality. If the proton is the canoe, the electron is the outrigger. As Richard Feynman pointed out, it is purely electrical.

We can understand the attraction between the proton and the electron as the undividedness seen in the duality, just as we can understand the gravitational attraction of the protons for each other as the undividedness seen in the plurality. As a member of the duality, the proton sees itself (if we may use such language) as separated from the electron. As a member of the plurality, it see itself as separated from the rest of the Universe. But in either case it sees itself as small, and we can understand the self-repulsion of like charge as simply the infinitude seen in the apparent smallness. The

One, Two, Three and Many

gravitational energy of the primordial hydrogen can be understood as Priya, the undivided seen in the apparently divided. The electrical energy of the primordial hydrogen can be understood as Bhati, the infinite seen in the apparently finite. Bhati and Priya drive the change in which the changeless is seen as Asti, inertia. In the great-space, this is our primordial hydrogen. It arises through apparition, through the appearance of pairs of opposites, space against time, mass against energy, gravity against electricity, plus against minus and spin-up against spin-down, without any change in the changeless.

MAYA

We have seen how, through relativity theory, modern science has been driven to the conclusion of the Advaita Vedantins that the first cause must be apparitional. The screen through which we see the reality must be the screen of apparitional causation – what the Vedantins call Maya. We have also seen how, through relativity theory, modern science has been driven to the conclusion that the nature of the reality which underlies the multifarious diversity in the world of our perceptions must be changeless, infinite and undivided. Finally, and this is the important point, we have seen that, through a careful analysis of apparitional causation we are able, at last, to understand why we see a Universe of hydrogen and not something else.

The Breath of Uncertainty

One of the problems which arises when we mistake a rope for a snake is that it is impossible for us properly to identify the snake. We cannot determine whether it is a Russell's Pit Viper or a Cobra. Not only can we not determine the species of the snake, but if we examine it too closely we'll find hemp fibers at the ends and a three-strand spiral winding. A similar problem shows up in our physics. If, through apparitional causation, we see the underlying reality as a Universe in space and time, then, within that Universe, there appear certain details which have proved to be beyond the possibility of finding out.

The Universe is made of hydrogen. The hydrogen is made of electricity. And the electricity takes the form of protons and electrons which hold their distance from each other. Why? We say that the proton is a positive charge and the electron is a negative charge, and we know that the attraction between positive and negative charges is surpassingly great. We may get an idea of the magnitude of that attraction if we consider two grains of sand each one millimeter in diameter and placed about seventy-five feet apart. If one of these grains of sand were made entirely of positive charges and the other, entirely of negative charges, then the electrical pull between them would be equivalent to the pull required to pick up one hundred and eight, fifty thousand ton battleships strung together as a rosary. Since at half that distance the pull would be four times as great and at a thousandth of that distance it would be a million times as great, we cannot handily overlook the pull, even between a single proton and its electron, at the distance of their proximity in an atom. Yet the electron will not sit down. Why?

It is simply because of this breath of uncertainty which necessarily plagues our perception of a Universe of mass and energy seen in space and time. The reason for the uncertainty may be simply illustrated.

AN ILLUSTRATION

If three golf balls are placed on the floor near the center of a darkened room, and if

The Breath of Uncertainty

several persons, each with a bag of ping pong balls, are seated around the edge of the room, then the people around the edge of the room can discover the positions of the golf balls by rolling their ping pong balls against them in the dark. The ping-pong balls, being much lighter than the golf balls, will bounce off the latter without seriously moving them. It would be impossible, however, to discover the positions of ping-pong balls by rolling golf balls against them since the impact of the golf balls would destroy the information being sought.

The problem of determining the position and momentum of the electron in the hydrogen atom is quite similar. With what shall we bombard it so as to disturb it as little as possible and yet get back the information? Bombarding it with a proton is like rolling a golf ball at a ping-pong ball. It's like trying to find out about butterflies with a hatchet. It's too destructive to the butterflies. Even another electron is too massive for our ammunition. And if we turn to radiation the problem is no nearer solution, since the radiation itself comes in discrete packages (photons), and the energy of an ultraviolet photon is enough to knock the electron away from the proton entirely. If we go to photons of lower energy we find that they are associated with longer wavelengths, and, when the wavelengths become long with respect to the distance across an atom, they can no longer carry information about the position of the electron within the atom. It would be like measuring the length of a beetle with an odometer.

Heisenberg's famous uncertainty principle is the result of a careful investigation of the limitation thus imposed on the physical measurement of a physical system. Any apparatus which we may set up to allow us to measure accurately the position of a particle makes it impossible for us, simultaneously, to measure accurately its momentum. Likewise, any apparatus which we may set up to allow us to measure accurately the momentum of a particle makes it impossible for us, simultaneously, to measure its position. There is a necessary uncertainty in our measurements such that the product of our uncertainty in the position of a particle and our uncertainty in its momentum can never be less than a certain small amount designated as Planck's constant, h, over two pi.

$$\Delta x \; \Delta mv \geq h / 2\pi$$

Now if the electron were to sit on the proton, then the uncertainty in its position would be so small that the necessary uncertainty in its momentum would drive it off. Why? Because we cannot have a large uncertainty about a very small quantity. One could not mistake the weight of a mouse by a pound or a ton. If an electron is sitting on a proton, the uncertainty in its momentum must be so large that the momentum associated with that uncertainty is enough to drive it off.

THE UNCERTAINTY

The existence of the hydrogen atom itself, then, depends on this uncertainty. And the uncertainty arises from the necessary interaction between the perceiver and the perceived, or, rather, between the instrument of perception and the object perceived. We know now, from our physics, that the perceiver is always mixed up in what he sees. Every portrait of the Universe is signed. Every description of the physical Universe is made from the standpoint of some perceiver associated with some instrument of perception.

Now the very curious thing about this situation is that the behavior of matter is itself determined by what we can and cannot know. It is a little like the stock market. The behavior of the stock market depends on the ignorance of those who play it.

The Universe is made of hydrogen, yet the hydrogen atom itself, like any apparition, exists only because of this breath of uncertainty.

'NUCLEAR ENERGY'

It can easily be shown that nuclear energy is related to this uncertainty, and that only if our uncertainty in the position of an event in space and time were total, could the momentum and the energy associated with that event go to zero. As George Gamow pointed out long ago, it is the increased uncertainty in the position of the charge in a deuteron (one electron on *two* protons) which allows the uncertainty in the momentum (and, therefore, the momentum associated with that uncertainty) to fall. An electron confined to a single proton will jump away, whereas an electron confined to two will not.

The larger the nucleus the larger the uncertainty in position and, therefore, the lower the associated momentum. It is only the disruptive effect of the increased electrical charge that raises the electrical energy (not the nuclear energy) of larger nuclei, rendering them less and less stable beyond iron, and radioactive beyond uranium. If, and only if, our uncertainty in the position of a charge were total could its momentum fall to zero. And only if our uncertainty in the time of an event were total could its energy (the time component of the momentum) fall to zero. If you can know where something is in space and time, you've bought the whole can of worms.

To know where something is, is to know where it is with respect to other things. And to know where something is, is to know that it is small enough so that its position could be accurately determined. The only reason that the distances from city to city can be designated on a road map to within a mile, is because the measurements are made from post office to post office, and the post offices are small with respect to a mile.

ENERGY ARISES BY APPARITION

To know were a proton is, is to know its position with respect to all the other matter in the observable Universe, and then the undividedness will show through as its gravitational energy. Also, to know where the proton is, is to know that it is small, and then the infinitude will show through as its electrical energy. It has already been pointed out that its gravitational and electrical energies are the same thing. They are two sides of one coin. But if they are the two sides, the nuclear energy is the edge of that same coin. They are all the same thing. Energy is apparitional. Only its changes are transformational. To see anything in space and time is to see the Universe which we see.

The Breath of Uncertainty

The two great changes which have come in our physics since Swamiji's day are relativity theory and quantum mechanics, and each is associated with a paradox. Relativity, as we have seen, in its effort to save the objectivity of the Universe, had to throw in the sponge on the separation between the perceiver and the perceived on which the concept of objectivity was based. Here, in quantum mechanics, we see our second paradox. The most certain of our certain knowledge of physics is now stated in terms of quantum mechanics and yet our entire knowledge of quantum mechanics rests on this unavoidable uncertainty.

From the Borders of the Universe

When we look out on this strange, apparitional Universe, we see that all the distant galaxies appear to be moving away from us, and the farther away they appear to be from us, the faster they appear to be moving away. The evidence for this expansion, and it is usually thought of as an expansion, is the redshift of the spectral lines in the radiation from those distant galaxies.

THE DOPPLER SHIFT

(When a fire engine is approaching us at high speed, we hear the sounds of the bell and the siren at a higher pitch than the pitch which is heard by the firemen on the engine. But, when the engine has passed us and is receding from us, we hear the sounds at a lower pitch. This is called the Doppler shift, and we see the same thing in radiation. The spectral lines of an approaching star are shifted toward the blue end of the spectrum while the spectral lines of a receding star are shifted toward the red end, the low energy end, and are said to be redshifted.)

Beyond Time and Space

Now this cosmological expansion, as it is called, imposes a boundary on the observable Universe, because beyond a certain distance, even if there were galaxies, we couldn't see them. They would be moving away at speeds in excess of the speed of light and it would be impossible for us to see them. It would be impossible for us, by any measurement, to determine the existence of such matter. Radiation from there could never reach us, the gravitational fields could never reach us, nor could any message however contrived.

REDSHIFT IMPOSES THE BORDER

Actually, it is the redshift itself, rather than our interpretation of the redshift, which imposes this boundary, and it is an observational boundary, not an actual boundary. It is not a boundary which could be visited. The observer is always at the same distance from it, in all directions, and, at the present observed rate of expansion, this boundary should be about fifteen thousand million light years away (fifteen American billion).

From the Borders of the Universe

Are there any messages from the borders of the Universe which reach us here, and which could be interpreted as evidence that such a boundary does, indeed, exist?

MESSAGES:

THE FIRST

Yes, there are. There are several such messages, and one of them is apparent even to the unaided eye. The night sky is dark. We must not let the familiarity of the observation keep us from understanding its significance. If the observable Universe were infinite in extent, and if it were speckled with stars as we see it nearby, and if the stars were "forever," then as Kepler and others long ago pointed out, the entire night sky should be as bright as the face of the Sun. Under such conditions, looking in any direction which we choose to look, we would see the face of a star with a surface brightness as least approximately equal to the surface brightness of the Sun.

Partly the night sky is dark because the redshift of the radiation from the distant galaxies which we *can* see robs that radiation of some of its energy. But mostly the night sky is dark because the redshift of the radiation from *beyond* about fifteen billion light years away would rob that radiation of *all* of its energy so that we could see nothing at all.

THE SECOND

A second such message is related to the rest mass of matter nearby and is apparent to the unaided hand. If the observable Universe were infinite in extent, and of a mean density comparable to the mean density nearby, then the rest mass of matter would be infinite and it would be impossible to shake a stick.

Each proton sees itself separated from all other protons in the observable Universe, and the gravitational energy involved in this separation is the gravitational rest mass of the proton. It is matched, of course, by its electrical rest mass due to the smallness of the electrical charge. They are two sides of the same coin. Now, with the present known strength of the gravitational field, if the number of protons from which each proton saw itself separated were infinite, then its gravitational energy (its mass) would, likewise, be infinite. Once again, we must not allow ourselves to be thrown by our familiarity with the observation. *A finite rest mass can arise only in a finite Universe.*

THE THIRD

There is a third message, not so obvious, arising from the extreme redshift of the radiation from very near the border. If, as seen by us, most of the energy of that radiation is redshifted away, then, as seen by us, most of the energy of the particles giving rise to that radiation will also be redshifted away. Then, since $E = m$, the mass of those particles will be seen to be very low, and the radiation moving through the vicinity of those low mass electrical particles will be so often absorbed and re-radiated as to reach us thermalized to a black body radiation at about 3 degrees Kelvin. If an observational boundary such as we have suggested does really exist, then this thermalized black body radiation should reach us from all directions in space. Such a microwave background radiation was discovered in the 1960's and is interpreted by the proponents of the "big bang" hypothesis as the radiation of the fireball cooled by some fifteen billion years of expansion. But it is unavoidable even in the steady state model.

THE FOURTH

A fourth message, if it may be considered to be a message at all, depends, as so many cosmological messages do depend, on the model of the Universe that is assumed in the interpretation of the evidence. It is related to the density of the Universe and, once again, it is not immediately apparent.

THE BIG BANG

For a "big bang" model, a model which explains the apparent expansion of the Universe as due to a cosmic explosion, a gradual decrease in the overall density of matter in the Universe is acceptable. It is not acceptable, however, for a steady state model which assumes that the expansion is beginningless and is driven by the energy which the radiation loses in its long traverse of the vast, expanding spaces of the Universe. A

From the Borders of the Universe

Universe of finite density cannot result from a beginningless expansion without some mechanism to prevent its decrease in density. Either there must be a mechanism for the creation of new matter within it, or there must be a mechanism for the recycling of material from the boundary back into the observable Universe. Is there such a mechanism?

RECYCLING

Curiously enough, there is. And it arises through Heisenberg's uncertainty principle. As the rest mass of the particles near the boundary is seen to approach zero, the momentum of those particles is also seen to approach zero, and if the momentum approaches zero, then our uncertainty in that momentum must also approach zero. But, by the uncertainty principle, if our uncertainty in the momentum of a particle approaches zero, then our uncertainty in its position must approach totality, and there is then no measurement whatsoever by which we could determine that the particle is near the boundary. If the uncertainty in the position

151

goes to totality, the particle may be found *anywhere*. This should give rise to a rain of "brand new" hydrogen throughout the observable Universe.

A STEADY STATE THEORY

It should be noted that this steady state model does not suggest that the expansion of the Universe should be constant in time or homogeneous throughout space. Nor does it suggest that the size of the observable Universe should remain constant. It only suggests that there should be some sort of mechanism to bring it back to some sort of norm.

If, for instance, the expansion rate were somehow doubled, the receding galaxies would reach the speed of light at about seven and a half billion light years from us instead of the currently estimated fifteen billion. Then the protons would see themselves separated from a smaller number of other protons, and their rest mass would thus decrease. But if their rest mass decreases, the rate at which they would fall together by gravity would likewise decrease. Then the radiation rate which drives the expansion would go down and the boundaries of the observable Universe would again recede, raising the rest mass of the protons. Similarly, if the expansion rate were slowed, the boundaries of the observable Universe would recede from us. The proton mass would consequently rise, increasing the radiation rate, which, in turn, would increase the expansion rate and bring the boundary back in.

Life

We come now to the problem of living organisms, including ourselves: How do we fit into this grand scheme? The problem, at first sight, seems insurmountable since the grand scheme, as we have sketched it, arises through apparition, yet the apparition itself implies a perceiver, and perceivers, *as we know them*, are embodied in forms which imply billions of years of preliminary, transformational evolution. The chemical elements of which the earth is made required billions of years of galactic and stellar evolution for their manufacture in the stellar interiors, for their distribution through interstellar space by explosions and stellar winds, and for their subsequent accumulation in the clouds of dusty hydrogen from which our Sun was born. Then, following the formation of the earth from that solar nebula, the development of such a complicated organism as man required another several billion years of genetic evolution, from the time of the blue-green algae through the simple poly-celled organisms, the mud worms, the chordates, the vertebrates, the fish, the finbacks, the mammals, and, finally, among the mammals, the primates, including man. (There is, of course, nothing final about it. We think of it as final only because we see it from our own point of view). All these things arise by transformational causation from the apparitional hydrogen, but how can the apparitional hydrogen exist without perception?

THE NATURE OF PERCEPTION

First we must ask: What is perception? We think of ourselves as perceivers, but we are smart enough to understand that our sense of perception is associated with the consciousness of a highly evolved, multi-celled organism with an elaborate brain made up of billions of individual cells. And we also understand that we are not, in any way, aware of the consciousness or the perceptions of the individual cells of which our bodies or even our brains are composed.

Life

Is perception limited to such poly-celled organisms or do the individual cells have their own perceptions? We know that the individual cells do have their own perceptions, or at least that they respond to the same sort of stimuli as those to which we, as poly-celled organisms, respond. In fact, our own sense perceptions depend entirely on the fact that even single protoplasmic cells respond to gravity, kinetic energy, radiation, electricity and magnetism.

The interesting thing is that just as our sense perceptions depend on the perceptions, or at least the responses, of single protoplasmic cells, just so the perceptions, or responses, of the individual cells depend on the responses of the individual atoms to those same five forms of energy. Even the primordial hydrogen atoms respond to gravity, kinetic energy, radiation, electricity and magnetism. What they don't do is show any evidence of individual will in their responses. This manifestation of what we see as individual will is a characteristic of what we call living organisms and we shall examine it in some detail, but what we see as perception originates at the atomic level. It arises in "square one."

ATOMIC PERCEPTION

Every atom of hydrogen in the primordial apparition is gravitationally aware of every other atom. It is subject to falling by gravity, radiating when bumped, and is made of electrical particles which respond to the electrical and magnetic fields. All transformational causation depends on this native atomic sentiency. The problem of how could the apparition exist in the absence of perception does not, therefore, arise.

'THE QUICK AND THE DEAD"

The question that does arise is: How do we fit into this scheme? How is it that we seem to have energy of our own, the so-called "vital energy"? And what is the difference between the quick and the dead?

As Erwin Schrodinger pointed out in his little book *What is Life?*, every living organism has the problem of directing upon itself a stream of negative entropy. If it succeeds, it is alive. If it fails, it is dead.

Life

Entropy is a measure of the scrambledness of energy. Every machine, and every living organism, scrambles the energy in its environment, and must, therefore, have a source of energy less scrambled at the start. *For all embodied beings, negative entropy is food.* For a vulture on a mountain slope, feeding on the carcass of the deer, his source of negative entropy is the reducing agents in the carcass of the deer, and the oxidizing agency of the air which he breathes. For the deer, it was the reducing agents in the plants which she ate, and the oxygen in the air which she breathed. For the plants, the source of negative entropy, by which they produce both the reducing agents which we eat as well as the free oxygen in the atmosphere which we breathe, is the radiation of the Sun. Finally, for the Sun, its source of negative entropy is the dispersed, primordial hydrogen, falling together by gravity, and that negative entropy arose by recycling and not by any transformation.

Beyond Space and Time

NEGATIVE ENTROPY ARISES BY APPARITION

Locally, the Universe appears to be running down. The usability of the energy is running down. Gravitational energy, which is completely usable, completely unassociated with entropy, is being converted to kinetic energy, then to radiation and so forth, and at almost every step the entropy increases. Occasionally it remains unchanged, but it never goes down. It is easier to scramble an egg than to unscramble it. *All living organisms live in this cascade of increasing entropy by channeling bits of the increase through their forms.* That is what we feel to be our vital energy. It seems to be our own. Really, it is not. The source of negative entropy is not in us, but in the environment in which we live. If we give up eating and breathing, what we feel as our vital energy will promptly run down.

CHANNELING NEGATIVE ENTROPY

Life does not exist in what the chemists call a state of equilibrium. If the energies of the Universe ever reach equilibrium, life will be snuffed out. It is only the universal cascade of increasing entropy that makes life possible.

Life

And life is always a struggle. Always the channeling of negative entropy requires discrimination on the part of the organism, not the discrimination between the perceiver and the perceived, but between the organism and its environment, between the eater and its food.

DISCRIMINATION

That is where our ego comes in. It is a gene pool invention, related to the necessity of this discrimination. And, through the long course of genetic evolution, the forms of this discrimination have become so vastly proliferated that by now the ways in which the various life forms channel the negative entropy upon themselves have become innumerable and almost unbelievably intricate. Through the discrimination between light and dark, the plant must spread its leaves to catch the Sun. Through the discrimination between plants of different species, the deer must browse. The snake must take the frog and leave the stones. Unfortunately, the discrimination between food and eater is not objective, so that, to quote the *Panchamahabhuta Sutras*, "What to one is body, to another is food." The deer sees herself as eater and the grass as food, but the tiger stalks the deer, and the vulture waits.

REPRODUCTION

There is another characteristic by which we discriminate between the quick and the dead, between the animate and the inanimate, and that is the ability of the animate to reproduce their kind. In order that an *individual organism* should survive, it is necessary for it to direct a stream of negative entropy upon itself. In order that a *race of organisms, a species*, should survive, it is also necessary that the individuals have a mechanism for passing the genetic code to a future generation. And, to a very large extent, that is where our problems arise.

It is through this mechanism that we have the wool pulled over our eyes. For the survival of the species, it is necessary that the offspring should survive and reproduce, but it is not necessary that they should flourish. It is not necessary that our life should be painless. And it is not necessary that our understanding of

Life

the Universe should be correct. It is necessary only that it should be adequate for our survival and for our reproduction. It is true that through this natural selection, as it is called, we have come a long way. Our own species, at least, has reached a point where correct knowledge has become possible. But if we owe the genes our eyes, we owe them also the wool that is pulled over them. Our problem now is to get rid of the genetic confusion. Our problem is to discriminate, not between the organism and its environment, but between the real and the genetic make-believe.

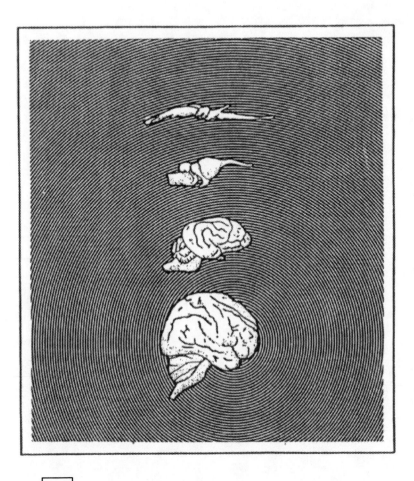

IV Sadhana

In What Furnace Was Thy Brain?

We have talked at some length about the nature of the reality, and about the apparitional screen through which we see it. And we have seen how we, as living organisms, genetic inventions if you like, see that screen much colored by our own genetic past. We have talked of Advaita Vedanta as a map, and we have talked about the map of modern science. And we have seen that the maps are easily joined since the advent of relativity theory. We have seen how even the quest of modern science, through the extrapolation suggested by relativity theory, has reached its fulfillment – the utterly simple – the Brahman of the Vedanta – which must underlie the obvious complexities of the physical Universe.

For us, as living beings, as travelers, what remain to be discussed are the paths, the trails, the possible journeys, which follow from the map. What remains to be seen is how the variety of sublime vistas which unfold before the eyes of the traveler fit into the map. And what remains to be known is how to get from our present state of perception to the goal.

SEEING BEYOND THE SCREEN

The goal is to know the truth, to see beyond the screen, to see the reality as it is, and the goal is to be reached by means of a path, by means of a journey, and not by means of a map. If one is to drive a bus from San Francisco to the Grand Canyon of the Colorado, one does not drive the bus over the map, but over the intervening highways and freeways, and there are many things to be seen along the way.

THE MAP AND THE JOURNEY

Modern science and the philosophy of Advaita Vedanta are our map; Sadhana is our journey. With the help of the map we choose a road, we choose a course of Sadhana (spiritual practice), and along that road, however long, however beset by seeming trials, we journey, through regions ever more sublime, till the goal is reached. We journey till we see, at last, that the goal itself was never distant and that the journey was but part of the screen.

In What Furnace Was Thy Brain?

Now a course of Sadhana, like a bus route, must take into account our point of origin as well as our destination, and our point of origin is deeply involved in our long genetic past. Far down the genetic line in this menagerie of living forms, and late in time, we come to inherit the peculiar problems of our kind, not those of the butterfly who wears her skeleton outside, nor, any longer, those of a fish. But look at your face in a mirror! Your jaw still swings like the jaw of a bony fish, which once you were, some four hundred million years ago. And the bones of that fish must shape your Sadhana. Sadhana, in a sense, is not the beginning of anything. It is simply the continuation, with better knowledge, of your age-old struggle to see the real, and it starts from where you find yourself in that struggle.

WHO ARE WE?

We are primates, brachiating primates, come from the green-roofed jungle by way of a sojourn in the Indian Ocean and the warm, sunny beaches of East Africa. The salt tears which we shed in the course of our Sadhana are the tears of a sea-going primate. The hands with which we do the worship are the hands of a jungle ape, reshaped by swimming in the sea. And our brain, our precious brain, the only brain on the face of this planet which allows the perceiver behind it to see through this apparition, is the brain of an ancient misfit, driven from one environment to the next so many times by the genetic hardware of better-adapted species that the software behind his eyes allows him now, at last, to see through the whole charade.

The following paragraphs are quoted from *The Moon Is New*, as yet unpublished.

For hundreds of millions of years you have been bullied and pushed around, driven from the ocean to the rivers, from the rivers to the shallows, from the shallows to the swamps, and out on land. Always the species who were better adapted to the older environment stayed in the older environment. The faster fishes stayed in the sea. You are not descended from them. You are descended from a long line of misfits who were bullied and driven out. Always it was "Shape up or get out!" and you got out.

In What Furnace Was Thy Brain?

You were driven ashore on stumpy fins in the Devonian swamps, and you were driven underground in the Paleocene grass, and you were driven from the grass into the trees, by other descendants of those stumpy fins. And every change entailed millions of years of discomfort while you painfully built in your new genetic adjustments, not so much by the survival of those who succeeded as by the early demise of those who failed. The dinosaurs, with scaly feet, drove some of you underground. Those who couldn't adjust are gone. There in their burrows, in the sunny grass, the rodents, furry mammals much like you, but better adapted to the grass than you, drove you to the trees. Those who couldn't adjust went down.

There in the trees, through long and painful genetic readjustments you learned to swing from branch to branch. Those who failed were eaten by cats. Then, after many more millions of years, just when your arms could reach from side to side, came the dwindling of the forests by drought, twelve million years of drought. Those who were better at swinging than you drove you to the ground, and you fled to the sea. You had four hands and no feet, and the grass was now no place for you. There were pack-hunting dogs and great, stalking cats. Those who didn't make it to the beach are gone.

In the safety of the terrifying breakers you were cradled in the sea, with hands instead of paddles and hands instead of feet, and there were millions of cold, wet, salty years before you even had the tears to cry. You were small and you were timid when you came from the green-roofed jungle with eyes accustomed to the dark, and there were millions of years of blinding brightness on the sunlit waves and beaches before you had the frown of your bewilderment, the furrowed brow of the thinker, and you wondered what it's all about.

The long pursuit has made you thoughtful. Every new adjustment entailed a genetic enlargement of the brain. It is the brain of a misfit, driven hither and yon to the refuge of new environments by those better adapted to the old. It is the brain of a shiftless outcast, living always in the discomfort of genetic maladjustment. It is the product of hundreds of millions of years of distress, the product of the vicissitudes of countless misfortunes encountered along the seemingly endless reaches of the immense journey. And your present form is not the end. The journey lies as far

In What Furnace Was Thy Brain?

ahead as behind. No, not so far, for now, for the first time, you can look behind to see how you have come. And now, for the first time, you can guess ahead to see how you should go.

In all that three hundred million years, no creature descended from the Snout, thought of himself as descended from the Snout, that lumbering, Devonian fish with simple lungs and bubbles in his brain. In all that length of time, no creature thought that any creature would ever think to figure it out, to unscramble and decipher the account. You are the first species that ever investigated its own genetic past. You are the only creatures who are not fish who ever knew that they are not fish but that their ancestors were. You are the first creatures who ever lived on land but who knew that their ancestors lived in the sea.

And you are the first creatures who can look ahead to see where you are going. You are the first creatures who can understand that you got into this mess through an uncertainty and cannot possibly get out by transformation. Uncertainty is overcome by knowledge, not by transformation. You alone can understand that the journey has an end, which cannot possibly be reached by journeying.

Beyond Space and Time

Yours is the strength of the eternal underdog. You have been pushed and bullied and driven till you have mastered every environment on the face of the earth, and have the brain to comprehend the Universe beyond. Out of the endless vicissitudes of your misfortunes and your failures has come your strength, and your love for the underdog. Every unbiased observer among you roots for the underdog.

When you walk in the woods, the squirrels don't bring you their peanuts, but you carry peanuts for them. The gulls don't bring you their lunches, but you throw your lunches to them. And signs are required at every zoo to keep you from feeding the underdog. Out of the strength to save yourselves has come the strength to save others. You are Eiseley's Star Throwers. Hundreds of millions of years of distress have gone into that strength, and the salt of those eyes.

For hundreds of millions of years, you have been bullied by the superior genetic technologies of better adapted species. You were hurt by the pincers of crabs, bled by the syringes of insects and killed by the syringes of snakes. You were scratched and torn by the talons and beaks of birds, crushed by the

In What Furnace Was Thy Brain?

hoofs of mammals, tossed by their antlers and gored by their horns. Losing the sea to the fins of faster fishes, long ago, and to the flukes of faster mammals, only yesterday, you came ashore again, only to be slashed by the fangs of cats, descended by another trail, another trial, from that same Devonian fish. Into every new habitat you came, you came lately. Everywhere you looked, there was someone ahead of you. Everything you could do, they could do better.

Every vicissitude of your misfortune had robbed you of some piece of genetic hardware which could have saved you in some niche, till, by the time you came, a second time, ashore, you had no fins, you had no flukes, you had no tusks, you had no claws, you had no hoofs, you had no fur. You were a ne'er-do-well's ne'er-do-well, protecting naked babies in the grass.

Without pincers, without syringe, without talons, without beak and without wings you came ashore, with no trunk, no hoofs, no fangs and no fur. But something else you had. Behind your furrowed brow you had a better brain. Every single blow of your misfortune, which drove you to another niche and robbed you of some piece of genetic technology, had hammered on its anvil some improvement in your brain till you had now the gleam of knowledge in your eye. At the cost of losing every piece of hard-won hardware, you have built the software behind your eyes. You have a brain to wonder and to understand.

And you have breasts to feed the growing brain of your helpless offspring. And you have tools, and you have words to tell your offspring how to use them. And you have fire to protect both your infant and your breasts from the bullying of furry beasts with fangs and claws and chattering teeth. Only in your nakedness have you lost your fear of fire, driven by the cold and by your terror of the hardware of other species. Your every misfortune you have turned to your account. Through the unfortunate necessity of prolonged parental care has come the growth of that brain that uses fire. Only through the prolonging of your youth has come your wisdom which began in the swamp, long ago, around those bubbles in your brain. You are the descendants of that ne'er-do-well, air-breathing fish, and the children of children who never grow up.

In What Furnace Was Thy Brain?

Now, for the first time, you have a software technology before which all the genetic hardware has gone down. Now, with non-genetic hardware, you out-swim the fish, you out-run the cats, you out-fly the birds, and you look down from the Moon, and you smile. Just think what went into that smile!

You have been pushed and bullied till you can be pushed and bullied no more. Every time you went down before the onslaught of some piece of genetic hardware you have come back with some unexpected improvement in the software behind your eyes, till now, with your software technology and the use of non-genetic hardware, you, the eternal underdog, can bully any species that ever bullied you. But with your new-won strength has come the frown of your puzzlement, the salt of your tears, and your smile. Why should dog eat dog? Why should a species, once bullied, bully back against the species that bullied it? The furrowed brow has noticed and the salty eyes are wet. You are the underdog's underdog, and now that hand, once fin, once paw, lengthened for swinging in the trees, and flattened for swimming in the sea, now that hand, grown old, reaches out to touch, in consolation, those who, in the past, have bullied it. Was it not their bullying that made you what you are? You are the Star Thrower, throwing the broken starfish back into the sea. Save the condor! Save the whales! Save the leopard! Save the shark! Save that menace of the seas against whose fearful jaws you learned to clench your fist!

You are the only creatures who ever knew that the rest of the creatures are just like you. You are the only creatures to have figured it out, that you got into this plight through an uncertainty and cannot possibly get out through a transformation. Knowledge is the key.

You are the first creatures to have figured out that the entire Universe is made out of hydrogen but that the hydrogen itself is an apparition. You are the first to see that your bodies, and every single terror that beset them in the past, arose, by transformation, from that primordial hydrogen, the colorless, odorless, tasteless, intergalactic gas, which couldn't possibly have arisen by any transformation, but only by the appearance of pairs of opposites on an underlying identity – plus against minus, electricity against gravity, and

In What Furnace Was Thy Brain?

*space against time – and that only on that identity
rests your concern for other creatures.*

*That ancient, bullied hand still reaches out.
That ancient, furrowed brow has understood, and
now the strength of knowledge lights those salty
eyes. The end is not far, and, to one who sees
beyond the transformations, the end is already
within reach. The journey has been immense, and,
in its immensity, it has yet to run, but the journey
has an end which cannot possibly be reached by
journeying.*

GENETIC REPROGRAMMING

We must start from where we are. We
cannot start from somewhere else. And where
we are is embodied in a form with a long
genetic past, with genetic predilections and
with genetic misprogramming on how to seek
the real. That is, we start with the
consciousness of our identity with such a form.
We are programmed to seek the changeless,
the infinite, the undivided, because there is
nothing else to seek. *There are no other goals.*
Toward that runs whatever runs. But we are
genetically programmed to seek the real

through actions which lead not to the perception of the real but, instead, to the production of viable offspring and to the survival of the species. Why? Because, in general, only the descendants of such programming have survived. We come from a long line of ancestors so strongly programmed in this direction that no one of them failed to leave offspring. But it is not that the problem alone is genetic; the solution also is partly genetic. Sri Ramakrishna used to say that when a man has a thorn stuck in his foot, he picks another thorn; then, with the help of the second, he removes the first and throws both thorns away. It is by understanding and making use of our genetic programming that we overcome our genetic problem.

SADHANA

Seen from the standpoint of our genetic programming, Sadhana is a device for counter-cheating the genes. The genes have us programmed to seek the real through action, through transformational causation. They have cheated us into the belief that through

In What Furnace Was Thy Brain?

action we can reach what we seek. But what we seek is beyond the screen thrown up by the apparition, while all action, its origin, its end and its means, exist within it. We are cheated into the belief that within time and space we can find and grasp that which is beyond all time and space. "He that drinketh of this water shall thirst again." Our problem is how to drink in such a way that the drinking erodes the apparition in which our thirst, itself, had its origin. Our problem is to do what we do in such a way that our discrimination and our renunciation destroy the screen.

Although the screen through which we view the reality is fundamentally apparitional, our viewing of the screen, our understanding of the screen, is largely the result of transformations. It is colored by our long genetic past, and therein lies part of our problem. Had it been a simple apparition, the solution to our problem would have been a simple piece of knowledge. But it is not at all that simple. We have this long genetic past through which we must worm.

Beyond Space and Time

The screen through which we glimpse the reality has become enormously complicated by the long series of genetic transformations through which our race has run. And, to a very large extent, our choice of journeys, as well as the vistas which unfold along the way, are dictated by that long genetic past. The reason that we offer, in our worship, the choicest fruits and flowers is because some hundred million years ago, about when we invented milk, the plants invented flowers and fruits, and the consequent spreading of the plants made possible the spreading of our ancestors across the land masses of this planet. The proliferation of the mammals awaited the spreading of the plants. The beauty of the flowers is not in the flowers, but in our own genetic response. It is not that beauty is in the eye of the beholder. Beauty is in the reality, but our ability to see it is under the thralldom of the genes. Where we would offer flowers, the vulture, surely, would offer a long-dead deer.

Counter-cheating the Genes

In order to counter-cheat the genes, we need to understand in what way they have cheated us. As James Burke says, "If you don't know how you got somewhere, you don't know where you are." And if we don't know where we are, how shall we know where to go? We must understand how we've been cheated by the genes.

INTUITION KNOWS

Hope springs eternal in the human breast. But why? After all your disappointments in love, and your frustrations, after being abandoned by your loved ones and your friends, and after finding that your own love is inconstant, still your intuition knows that love is true. Your intuition knows that freedom is true, although we never reach it here, and your intuition knows that peace is true. That intuition is just the nature of the real peeking through. Peace and freedom and love are just Asti-Bhati-Priya. They are just the nature of the reality seen through space and time. The oneness, which we see in the hydrogen as gravity, we feel in ourselves as love. The infinitude, which we see in the hydrogen as electricity, we feel in ourselves as our yearning for freedom. And the changelessness, which we see in the hydrogen as inertia, we feel in ourselves as our longing for peace. It is the Asti-Bhati-Priya referred to earlier. That is what drives whatever is driven, whether animate or inanimate. And, because there are no other drives to catch hold of, the genes have caught hold of those drives and re-directed them to drive us to the fulfillment of their biological necessities.

SPECIES SURVIVAL

A gene pool survives if, and only if, the genetic programming is such that the individual organisms fulfill certain biological necessities. At least the organisms must find and use a source of negative entropy, and must make some arrangement to pass on the genetic code. In our own case the fulfillment of these necessities has become somewhat complicated. Instead of just breathing, which is complicated enough, we make arrangements to breathe underwater with scuba gear and submarines, and we have even carried a breathable atmosphere to the Moon. Instead of just eating what we find, as a chimpanzee would, we breed edible plants and animals. We have farmers and ranchers and fishermen. And that's not all. We have cooks. We have invented such elaborate methods of preparing food that certain restaurants enjoy a worldwide reputation. Instead of just sleeping when tired, as so many animals do, we have beds and blankets, tents and sleeping bags, houses and mansions. And last, though certainly not least, our arrangements for passing on the genetic code have become so elaborate and so varied that whole cultures have grown up around them.

GENETIC CHANNELING

Our search for the changeless has been channeled by the genes to the preservation of our seeming self-identities, our egos, and to the enjoyment of rest and recreation. Our search for the infinite has been channeled to the direction of a stream of negative entropy upon our bodies and to the manifestation of power, to the pursuit of freedom for the body and the ego. But the body and the ego constitute the cage, not the lion. There may be such a thing as the freedom of a lion from the cage, but there is no talk of freedom for the cage. Likewise, there may be freedom from the ego, but there is no such thing as freedom of the ego.

Similarly, our search for oneness, our search for love, has been channeled by the genes to drive us to undertake actions which lead, not to the undivided, but to the bearing of genetic offspring. And, because our intuition knows that love is true, we have surrounded this genetic channeling with all sorts of romance and glamour – so much poetry, so many songs! But however complicated our patterns of fulfillment of these necessities have become, they are simply biological necessities which we are genetically programmed to fulfill, and every one of us is descended from a long line of ancestors no one of whom failed to fulfill them.

Counter-cheating the Genes

None of us is descended from a line of monks and nuns, and there lies our central problem. Although we are descended from large-brained primates, the manner of our genetic programming, that is, the method by which the programming is built in, is such that it has never been required that our genetic understanding of this Universe should be correct. It was required only that it should be adequate for staying alive and for bearing viable offspring. It was never required that we see space and time as opposites, or that we understand the origin of what we see as gravity. The equations of relativity theory were required to correct our native understanding of space, time and gravity, which most probably we hold in common with the seagulls and the dogs.

SQUARE ONE DRIVES OUR YEARNINGS

We are all programmed to fulfill these biological necessities, but fulfilling them does not fulfill our yearnings. *The fulfillment of a biological necessity does not confer on the organism the fulfillment of the yearning that drives it.* The yearning has been borrowed by the genes. The yearning is our vision of the real. There is just the changeless, the infinite, the undivided, seen through the screen of time, space and causation, which drives both the quick and the dead.

BUT THE GENES CHEAT

So long as the meal is not eaten, the yearning, channeled by the genes to the fulfillment of that necessity, drives the mind. Once the meal is eaten, once the biological necessity has been fulfilled, the mind is dropped like a wasted rag. That is why we meditate *before* we eat. So long as the actions required for passing the genetic code to a future generation have not been engaged in, the yearning drives the mind. As soon as they are completed, as soon as the biological necessity has been fulfilled, the mind is dropped like a wasted rag. That is why we practice Brahmacharya (monasticism). Unless, by cheating the genes of the biological fulfillment, we can turn the drive back to the real, what hope is there? The genes are the greatest cheaters in the world. They promise, through action, through transformational causation, to give us the changeless, the infinite, the undivided. But they cannot. Monasticism, and all Sadhana, is an effort to counter-cheat the genes, to correct our genetic misunderstandings, and, by re-directing our primary drives, which have been led astray by the genes, to turn them, once again, toward the unclouded vision of the real.

THE GENETIC MAKE-BELIEVE

Our minds are scattered by seeing the one as many. "As rain water, falling on a mountain peak, runs down the rocks in all directions; even so, he who sees the Dharmas (the Asti-Bhati-Priya) as separate, runs after them in all directions". -- Kathopanishad.

Whether as father, mother, children, wife or friend, or whether as peace or freedom or whatever, it is the real alone which we have sought, and that alone which we have perceived all along. There is nothing else to perceive. As Swamiji said, we do not go from error to truth but from truth to higher truth.

Beyond Space and Time

But through genetic manipulation, the desires of the ego have become proliferated, and there lies our problem. But the ego itself is genetic, and there lies our hope. As Sri Ramakrishna said, when the ego dies, all troubles cease.

The ego is simply a genetic invention arising from the necessary discrimination between the organism and its environment entailed in the direction of a stream of negative entropy upon itself. And Sadhana consists, essentially, of counter-cheating the genes at this point. It consists in redirecting that power of discrimination from fulfillment of the biological necessities to the discrimination between the real and the genetic make-believe.

BUDDHA'S APPROACH

Probably the sanest approach is that of Buddha, simply to recognize that the ego is an invention and transfer one's concern to the welfare of others – Bahujana hitaya bahujana sukhaya, for the good of the many, for the happiness and the welfare of the many. Swamiji wanted to see the worship of Daridra Narayana, God in the form of the poor. He wanted to see the Ganga running white with the washing of rice for feeding the poor. Worship is serving where service is needed, whether the offering be food or education or spiritual illumination. Let each serve where he can!

The counter-cheating device most used by the Advaita Vedantins is what they call the discrimination between the perceiver and the perceived. They make the discrimination, not between the organism and its environment as dictated by the genes, but between the perceiver and the perceived. It puts death in the perceived. Sri Ramakrishna used to speak of the ripe and the unripe ego. The unripe ego is the genetic ego. The discrimination is made between the organism and its environment, and the ego feels itself to be the doer, the knower, the enjoyer. In point of fact, the ego is not the doer. What we feel as our vital energy is not our own. It arises by apparition as the negative entropy of the primordial hydrogen. We simply direct a stream of that negative entropy upon our bodies from outside, from what we feel to be the external environment. Sri Ramakrishna used to say that only an ignorant person feels that he is the doer. Without that feeling, he becomes liberated in life. Man's sufferings and worries spring only from his persistent thought that he is the doer.

DIVINE MOTHER

What we see as action arises through Asti-Bhati-Priya, through the nature of the real showing through in the apparition. It is what Sri Ramakrishna referred to as Mother, the Divine Mother, the Blissful Mother, whom he used to say is made of consciousness. When he said, "Not I, but Thou," it was to her that he referred. The ripe ego, he said, is one that no longer says "I, I," but "Thou, Thou." He said that if this ego cannot be got rid of, then let the rascal remain as the servant or the child. That is, let it assume some interpersonal relationship, some genetic relationship, with the real. To re-direct one's genetic relationships in this way, away from the biological necessities which they were invented to fulfill, is, once again, to counter-cheat the genes. And the particular vistas which unfold before the eyes of the aspirant, the Sadhaka, are shaped, in part, by the particular relationship, or relationships, which he chooses to follow in his approach to the real.

EACH LIFE A PATH

Each life is like a separate piece of music. Each of us has his own past experiences to interpret, to understand and to use in his pursuit of truth. Each has his own favorite relationships which, when turned away from the fulfillment of the genetic necessities, may constitute, for him his most powerful tool. Each of us has his own trail, and each sees his own vistas.

THE PERSONAL AND THE IMPERSONAL

God is simply our highest vision of the real within the magic of Maya, within the clouds of the apparition. Each aspirant sees his own vision colored by his own past, both genetic and personal, and by his own expectations. Much colored by genetic expectations, we may see the real as personal. Colored by some other expectations, we may see it as impersonal. But the real is one. The snow-clad mountain peak is one, seen from whatever point of view, from east or west, whether lit by the rosy hues of dawn or by the blazing midday Sun.

Sri Ramakrishna used to say that God is both personal and impersonal, both formless and with form, and many are His forms which no one sees. He used to say that God's forms are like the icebergs frozen from the formless ocean by the intense cold of devotion, and subject to being melted away in the warm Sun of knowledge. The forms which we see are dictated largely by our own genetic past, but the real which we see in those forms is beyond the reach of Maya. We see God as Mother because primate babies take a long time to grow up and require a great deal of maternal care and affection. We owe the largeness of our brains, and all our Sadhana, to that. But the notion of mother will not so easily arise among the lizards or the fish.

THE FOUR MEANS

The Advaitins speak of four means of attainment which one must have if one is to see beyond the screen of this apparition: The discrimination between the real and the transient. The renunciation of the enjoyment of the fruits of action. The six treasures, calmness and the rest. And the yearning for liberation.

JNANA YOGA AND KARMA YOGA

The root cause of our trouble is that we have mistaken the rope for a snake and become snake fanciers. We have mistaken the changeless for the changing and seek our satisfaction in the changes. We have seen the real, which is one, as Asti-Bhati-Priya, which is many, and we run after it in all directions, watching the broken moonlight dance to extinction in the waves.

Our problem is to discriminate, not between the organism and the environment, which is a genetic discrimination, but, through an intellectual override, to discriminate between the real and the unreal. That is the root notion of Jnana Yoga, the path of knowledge. On the basis of this discrimination, we must give up the notion that we have anything to gain through action. That is the root idea behind Karma Yoga, the path of action. Action is to be done for others, without any expectation of return. The feeling that through action, through transformational causation within the apparition of space and time, we can attain the fulfillment of our primary yearnings, is at the base of our thralldom to the genes. Actions arise *within the apparition* by Asti-Bhati-Priya. The hydrogen is driven in contrary ways by inertia, electricity and gravity, and we by our yearning for peace and love and freedom. This world is made of frustration, and our hope for fulfillment through such actions is no more than a genetic mirage.

Shankara says that this discrimination and renunciation are like the two wings of a bird, in the case of a man. Without both, he cannot reach the creeper of liberation that grows, as it were, on the top of an edifice.

RAJA YOGA

The six treasures, calmness, self-control, the withdrawal of the mind from sense objects, forbearance, the enthusiastic conviction that the goal can be reached, and the resting of the mind on the real – all these six arise from the control of the mind. This control of the mind is the central idea in what is called Raja Yoga, the royal path. The mind is the instrument of our Sadhana, our bus, if you like. Knowledge and discrimination set the direction of our wheels, and renunciation drives the wheels along the road by pushing the road behind us. Progress is as much away from our point of origin as toward our destination. But our knowledge and discrimination as well as our renunciation are in the mind; so the mind must be kept strong if we are to reach the goal. It is through the mind that we feel our genetic programming, and through the mind that we must redirect it. Both bondage and freedom are in the mind.

Our yearning for freedom is said to be the fourth means of attainment. This yearning for freedom from the thralldom of the genes arises through knowledge, through discrimination. This devotion to the real arises through experience and through the conviction that our genetic drives are borrowed, that what we seek as peace and love and freedom exists only in the real. Even what the hydrogen seeks exists there alone. Seen within space and time, whether in us or in the hydrogen, it is a three-way frustration. Falling together by gravity is the opposite of flying apart by electricity, and both are the opposite of quiescence, or remaining inert.

BHAKTI YOGA

This yearning for the real is the basis of Bhakti Yoga, the path of devotion. Its essential practice is counter-cheating the genes by re-directing the genetic drives. If you must love, love Him! If you must hate, hate Him! Any genetic relationship, whether God is seen as father, mother, child, friend or loved one, may be used as a pole-star to guide the traveler through the trackless jungles of this phenomenal world.

Our problem is somehow to get from where we are to the goal, whether by knowledge or devotion, whether by skill in action or by control of the mind. Knowing the map, our task is to embark on our final pilgrimage.

The Pilgrimage

We have seen how the advent of relativity theory and quantum mechanics has changed the course of the stream of modern science, bringing it nearly parallel to the stream of Advaita Vedanta, which has come down from much earlier times. The confluence of these two streams has been made possible primarily by the suggestion, implied by both relativity theory and quantum mechanics, that there must be an apparitional causation underlying the transformational causations of our physics. Through the influence of relativity theory, the quest of our physics for the real in the external world has taken a new turn. It is not that the external world has been found to be unreal, but only that the real was not found to be external. The pre-relativity notion that there is a real separation between the perceiver and the perceived was misleading. The contrary notion, that the real is one and that the motions in what we see as the external world arise *only because the apparent separations are not real*, is the central notion of Advaita. It is to this notion that modern physics, by implication, points.

As was mentioned earlier, it is not that all physicists have accepted this suggestion, but we are here tracing the growth and development of concepts rather than their acceptance.

JOINING THE MAPS OF ADVAITA AND PHYSICS

What remained unclear at the edge of the map of Advaita was how the nature of Brahman, seen through Maya as Asti-Bhati-Priya, must show up in our physics. And what remained unclear at the edge of the map of our physics was why matter should appear as discrete electrical particles showing gravity and inertia. The unclear parts of these two maps were simply the region where the two maps join to make a single, more extensive map. The how of Advaita is in our physics and the why of physics is in Advaita. What was missing at the end of the last century was the knowledge of where the maps should be joined. Swami Vivekananda seems to have sensed where the maps should join. But his difficulty was that that section of the map had not yet been filled in by the physicists. Einstein was still a boy and Heisenberg was not yet born.

A BETTER MAP

A map, like a system of physics or philosophy, may be considered true if, and only if, it corresponds to fact. The physics of the last century did not correspond to fact. It did not correspond to the measurements of our physics nor to the experiences of the men and women of renunciation. What we needed was a map which would supply a philosophical backdrop against which we could better interpret not only the experiences of the men and women of renunciation, the Sadhakas, the saints, if you like, but against which, also, we could better interpret and understand our physics. That map we now have. But what is the use of such an extended map? Who needs it?

Beyond Space and Time

WHO NEEDS IT?

Maps are needed primarily by travelers, in this case by pilgrims, and the pilgrimage, for the charting of which this map is now needed, began long ago, not a few hundred or a few thousand years ago, but hundreds of millions of years ago in the genetic turmoil in which our brain was forged. Our ability to see unity behind diversity was built in there, through almost endless sorrows, around two bubbles in our brain.

THE END OF THE JOURNEY

For several hundred million years that pilgrimage has been made without a map, and that great genetic journey has yet to run. Whether this "immense journey," as Loren Eiseley calls it, will continue with or without a map, remains for living beings far in the future to see. But thus far it has been more or less aimless. It is possible that the goal may never be reached by the genetic trek of our descendants through the tangled jungles of biological necessity. It is only through a thousand strokes of good fortune, woven into the fabric of our misfortunes, that we have arrived at a point from which we can see the journey's end. And it lies, not ahead through the blind jungles of action in pursuit of genetic necessities, but off in a new and different direction through the open spaces of individual discrimination and renunciation. Through a smattering of good fortune mixed into the misfortunes of our long genetic trek, we have now arrived at a point from which each pilgrim can strike out on his own toward the goal. It is for that pilgrimage that our map is needed.

OUR PILGRIMAGE

The individual's pilgrimage from our present position in the blind genetic trek to the goal is still long but no longer uncharted. It is still a frontier country crossed originally by a few bold explorers and crossed more frequently, in later times, with the help of competent guides. But now the country is charted so that pilgrims in enormous numbers may cross with the help of an accurate map.

The journey from here, though made by many, must still be made alone, leaning on no one. It is a journey for the strong, the heroic.

Firm in our knowledge of the path, leaving all genetic actions behind, we forge ahead by discrimination. Retracing every yearning to the source from which it came, and leaving the dead to bury their dead, we go.

RAISING YOUTH WITH THE NEW MAP

Eventually it may be possible to improve the native genetic programming of the species but, for now, our hope lies here. We have the accumulated knowledge. What would happen if the young were trained in the knowledge of the map, unencumbered by the mass of genetic superstition which has come down to us from ancient times? Swami Vivekananda wanted the experiment tried. He wanted to see a group of children raised in the knowledge of Advaita. Let them know the truth alone, free from all genetic hocus-pocus, free from the notion that the Universe runs on the whims of a personality, however sublime.

DEMOCRACY AND THE VEDANTA

Historically, religion, even Vedanta, has been mixed up with the fatherhood of God, or the motherhood, or the kingship. They are much alike. Swamiji wanted it taught without that. He felt that the religions of a people reflected their social structure and that the religions of India had been vitiated by his majesty the king or her majesty the queen. He felt that democracy was the more suitable soil for the growth of Advaita. He said that in a democracy the king has entered into everyone.

Democracy has come now, first in America, then in France and now in India. Now is the time for Advaita, for the worship of "the other God, man." Swamiji said that if Vedanta, the conscious knowledge that all is one spirit, spreads, the whole of humanity will become spiritual.

Glossary

Ajatavada: The doctrine of non-birth, that birth
is unreal.

Akasha: Space. Also matter. It also means
gravitational energy which is associated
with space and matter, and is perceived
through the saccule in the ear.

Chidakasha: Consciousness space, where there
is only the duality of the seer and the seen.

Chittakasha: Mind space, the space of
interpersonal relationships.

Mahakasha: Great space, the space which
seems to separate the stars.

Ap: Electrical energy, perceived by the tongue.
(Protons taste sour.)

Apparitional causation: An apparent change,
as when you mistake a rope for a snake.
(Nothing happens to the rope.)

Atman: The Self, the breather, the perceiver.

Big Bang: The currently popular cosmological
model that explains the apparent expansion
of the Universe as due to a cosmic
explosion.

Brahman: The underlying existence, not in time

and space, changeless, infinite and
undivided.

Daridra Narayana: God in the form of the
poor.

Entropy: A measure of the scrambledness of
energy.

Gunas: Maya or the mistake of seeing things in
space and time is said to be made of three
Gunas, Tamas, Rajas and Sattva.

Heisenberg's uncertainty principle: There is a
necessary uncertainty in physical
measurements such that the product of our
uncertainty in the position of a particle and
our uncertainty in its momentum can never
be less than a certain small amount
designated as Planck's constant, h, over two
pi. A similar statement may be made with
respect to time and energy.

Inertia: The tendency of a body to resist
changes in its state of rest or motion.

Mach's principle: Inertia here depends on
inertia in the rest of the Universe.

Maya: The mistake of seeing things in space
and time.

Mumukshutvam: The yearning for liberation.

Glossary

Nuclear energy: The energy that's released by electrical rearrangements in the nucleus of the atom.

Panchamahabhutas: The five great elements of antiquity. They are five forms of energy perceivable by our five senses of perception. Akasha, or gravity, with the ear (the saccule), Vayu, or kinetic energy, with the skin, Tejas, or radiation, with the eye, Ap and Prithivi, electricity and magnetism, with the tongue and the nose. (Protons taste sour, and the nose matches magnetic structures in the molecules.)

Parinama: Transformational causation

Prakriti: The first cause, or Maya.

Purusha: Person. Often used as a synonym for Atman.

Rishis: Knowers in antiquity. Some were physicists.

Sadhana: Spiritual practice.

Shraddha: Spiritual enthusiasm, faith.

Square one: Apparitional physics.

Transformational causation: Causation by the transformation of energy from one form to another without any change in the amount.

Beyond Space and Time

Upanishads: The philosophical portions of the
ancient Sanskrit scriptures called the Vedas.
Vivartavada: The doctrine that the first cause is
apparitional, the mistake of seeing the
underlying existence as in time and
space.

Index

Beyond Space and Time

Index

Beyond Space and Time

Index

Beyond Space and Time

Index

Beyond Space and Time

Index

Printed in the United States
93197LV00005B/32/A